Notes from Africa

NOTES FROM
AFRICA

H. S. Aynor

FREDERICK A. PRAEGER, *Publishers*
New York • Washington • London

85856

FREDERICK A. PRAEGER, PUBLISHERS
111 Fourth Avenue, New York, N.Y. 10003, U.S.A.
5, Cromwell Place, London S.W.7, England

Published in the United States of America in 1969
by Frederick A. Praeger, Inc., Publishers

Library of Congress Catalog Card Number: 72–83783

Printed in the United States of America

TO
MY AFRICAN FRIENDS . . .
FAITH AND COURAGE

Contents

Preface

LATE AT NIGHT IN AN EMBASSY IN AFRICA. . . .
The Ambassador has sat up late compiling data, checking on figures, for a long report. He is tired now. The language of economics
is too mathematical and rigid for his mood. What he is really trying
to write about, he tells himself, is the impact of economic underdevelopment on the human being in Africa, but the human being
has been lost in the jargon.

*African agriculture and the deterioration of the terms of ex-
change:* "The underdeveloped nations are caught in a multiple
cycle of economic asphyxiation. . . ." He puts the report aside.
Ideally it should contain the essence of his experience in this country: his insights. But all he reads in it is his weariness. On an
impulse, he scribbles on his memo pad:

"Dear John: You will be surprised to receive this personal note as
an addendum to my unusually long economic report. I have been
stationed in Africa for over three years, as you know. Physically,
I am quite exhausted by the climate and by the work. Intellectually,
I have the feeling that I am becoming, with the passage of time,

ix

like a lonely mulatto—neither here nor there, neither fully trusted
nor fully understood by black *or* white. Africa is certainly a great
challenge, but the problems are enormous and strangely complicated, and there is little intellectual cooperation between us and
the Africans in the finding of the answers. Are there any chances of
an early transfer, do you think?"

He knows what John's reaction will be: he has become too *involved:* a good ambassador should have the detachment of a surgeon, a reporter. What could he do, he wonders, that would really
get through to the people at home? This report, even if it were read
properly, would simply be filed away. He glances at his diary at the
corner of his desk. Perhaps if he sent that instead, it would tell
more of what he had seen through his daily routine, the daily
rituals of a diplomat's life in Africa. . . .

Notes from Africa

ONE

The Cocktail Party

THE WEST COAST OF AFRICA. A LATE TROPICAL afternoon. The waves of the Atlantic drum lightly against the cliffs on the rocky shore. The capital, almost immersed in the deep green of tropical vegetation, emerges white and shimmering in the distance. From afar, a few tall buildings catch the eye—like hens surrounded by a numerous brood. A truck passes slowly, almost noiselessly, along the gray asphalt road following the shore line.

The deep sound of a tam-tam vibrates over the hot, tired town—disappearing, reappearing again from nowhere, and fading into the unknown—at once melancholic and mysterious. The shore road is almost deserted; now, a solitary figure may be seen, walking quietly to the beach. Here and there, a fisherman is silhouetted against the hazy deep blue of the horizon. Above the rocky beach, white and black diver birds on the lookout for a catch sail in the evening sky.

The first black, beflagged limousines appear round the bend in the road. Seven o'clock, cocktail hour, has arrived.

3

In much of Africa, this cumbersome European custom still re-
tains some purpose. In a one-party state, where all means of information are tightly controlled if not censored, news is hard to
come by, information and rumor go hand in hand and are difficult to check. Everyone plays the game of "Who, When, Where,
and What-Is-Going-On?" and very few know anything reliable—
except maybe the head of state himself.

In particular, diplomats, whose profession it is to be informed,
are constantly exposed to rumors of all sorts: the Minister of
Health falling out with the President over regional (meaning
tribal) party politics; the Minister of the Armed Forces—is he or
is he not *persona non grata* after the speeches and interviews he
gave abroad were reported here, or is he perhaps too well liked by
those young and unruly officers? One astonishing and frustrating
feature for the diplomat is that his African friends—ordinary citi-
zens and high officials alike—in the privacy of their offices ask him
the ever-repeated question "What is going on?" The lack of
knowledge and reliable information concerning local or African
matters is all-pervading.

So the cocktail party is a necessary bazaar—to find out, for instance, whether the laying of the new water pipeline in the city
has been allotted to that German firm or whether the matter is
still in abeyance; whether or not import quotas for pharmaceuticals
will be amended to include British and American products;
whether the rumors about some sudden and mysterious deaths
through cholera in the north are based on fact. Was last Friday's
student demonstration at the university directed against the administration or against the war in Vietnam? Who was invited to
the President's dinner party last Sunday? Is it true that a Scandinavian government has promised to send a team of physicians and
nurses into the interior?

The Ambassador is awaiting his guests. He is a lean, graying
man in a dark linen suit, tired and dehydrated by the humid
heat of tropical Africa, disillusioned but wiser after years of service
on the spot. His wife is in Europe, as are most of the Europeans'

wives during the hot season. Standing at his left are the two
guests from home in whose honor the party is being given. A short
heavy-set, blond man in a blue serge suit—he is mopping the
perspiration off his brow—is the newly appointed Director of the
Foreign Ministry's International Aid and Assistance Division; he
is on his first visit to Africa. The second guest looks out of place,
somehow—tall, muscular, mahogany-complexioned, white-haired,
mustached, he could be any age. He looks just like what he is:
an agronomist who has spent most of his life managing one of the
largest rubber plantations in Java; now he is Chief Agricultural
Expert in the Foreign Ministry.

The first guests arrive—presentations and handshakes. Instinctively, everyone searches out the coolness in a dark corner of the
drawing room, which opens on its far side onto a well-kept garden
where chairs and tables are conveniently arranged in the shade
of high trees. It is still too hot out of doors, but with sundown
and the light evening breeze, the guests will soon venture into
the open.

The diplomats are the first to come, repaying the courtesy of
their host, who is known for his punctuality and conscientiousness
in attending his colleagues' parties. Every one of the two dozen
missions in the capital is represented by its head or its chargé
d'affaires. This is a special occasion, and all heads of foreign assistance and aid missions have been invited as well. *They* are of
a different breed altogether. They bear themselves aloofly, but
they are less polished and less discreet than the diplomats—more
relevant and methodical, less inclined to small talk. They also are
an exceedingly serious lot, conveying a sense of great self-impor-
tance. Their technical and scientific training and functions are apparent to everyone. These men are responsible for thousands of
European and American technicians, teachers, and professionals
working on almost all the economic and cultural problems this
nation has. They control the funds their countries put at Africa's
disposal; they employ tens of thousands of local men and women.
They themselves are convinced that without their services, this
country—indeed, all Africa—would simply be incapable of run-

ning its administration, its army, its economy, or its education and would regress to some primitive chaos. Yes, they are the Very Important People of modern Africa, for the good reason that they are most sincerely convinced of their own importance.

A permanently-felt tension exists between them and their diplomatic colleagues, on both the personal and the professional levels. An Ambassador is the head of his nation's embassy, and without his consent and confirmation, nothing can be accomplished concerning this African nation—either back home or here on the spot. But in the technical experts' opinion, and they document this well, diplomats are a lower form of human life, created solely for the purpose of interfering with the professional men doing a straightforward and necessary job that should have been done long ago. They understand neither finances nor techniques nor computer planning, they speak on topics they never fully grasp, and in general they are hopelessly outdated, wasting most of their time on social niceties of no consequence whatsoever. Without them, everything would go better.

From the diplomats' point of view, their overpaid and overly independent technical advisers are undisciplined simpletons with no understanding of the intricacies of international and local politics and no feel for the importance of cultured social relations. A technician is responsible for building bridges, roads, factories, agricultural projects, but his world begins and ends with these matters. He loses sight of the ever-changing political situation and focuses on the relatively unimportant but expensive jobs to be done deep in the bush. Even worse, the technician has no flexibility. He will never change his approach or adapt his tactics. He is ready to criticize and vilify his own colleagues for not helping him, for not obtaining more funds, personnel, or supplies— and he will contradict and even offend an African administration up to the minister himself, making him personally responsible for the breakdowns and delays in his working schedule, financing, technical appointments, and labor supply. A senior ambassador once said, "A technician in Africa is a man on the run, in a continent where walking very slowly is a tremendous exertion."

A tall, balding blond man now joins the party and greets a group of colleagues. He is the Ambassador of a Scandinavian country, well-known and liked for his sarcastic wit. It is common knowledge that he is currently facing difficulties centered around a veterinary aid project in the arid north, where semi-nomadic tribes, mostly of the Fulani ethnic group, raise hundreds of thousands of sick and skeletal cattle. A year ago, the Ambassador had been approached by the highest authorities of the land on the matter of improving this cattle stock, and, after some hesitation, his country—world famous for its dairy products—agreed to conduct, at its own expense, a veterinary survey to establish the number of cattle in the north, to collect data on the most serious diseases, and to arrive at tentative economic conclusions concerning the establishment of a small modern dairy industry and slaughterhouse, aimed at freeing the country from the burden of importing meat from Europe. Some time was consumed by visits of experts and study missions. Various agreements were signed. But finally the day came when the field crew arrived, headed by a famous veterinary specialist. Then the trouble started.

The Minister of Agriculture, who had started the project, a scion of a well-known and aristocratic Fulani family, had by now moved one step along in his political career and had been named Minister of the Interior. The new Minister of Agriculture showed an obvious, and sophisticated, reluctance to approve the entire project. Coming as he did from the swampy forests of the south, he was convinced of the absolute priority of rice cultivation for national consumption and the need to establish banana plantations to give the country an export crop for trade with Europe. As a consequence, our Scandinavian veterinary mission found itself stranded: no light airplanes suitable for aerial photography appeared to be available, nor could the ten needed Land Rovers, with staff, be found. The great specialist and his assistants took an involuntary and lengthy vacation at the seaside. The younger members of the team took the incident in good humor, but not so the famous specialist, for he had been cheated out of the eye-catching scientific paper on this important subject which he had planned to present at an international conference later in the year. So he pestered and accused the Ambassador, wrote letters to ministers and newspapers back home; questions were raised in parliament, and an opposition member even demanded a parliamentary inquiry into the country's entire foreign aid and assistance policy. After four weeks of frantic and futile activity, making himself very unpopular with the entire African administration, the Ambassador finally decided that the continued good relations of his country were best served by getting rid of the veterinary and his crew, leaving the bovine population unstudied and unaccounted for. The aid mission departed, fuming, for home.

Now, surrounded by sympathetic colleagues, a cool drink in hand, the Ambassador relates the story of this adventurous failure. Together with advisers and veterinary technicians, he had recently visited one of the tribal units owning a huge herd of these decrepit cattle, and was hospitably welcomed by its venerable chief, one Hajj Umar. Hajj Umar served them sour milk, bread, and salt and showed much interest in the forthcoming census, asking many questions in broken French, and finally told the Ambassador the following tale:

"After the Second World War, my people were left with almost no livestock, very hungry and poor. One bright morning, the prefect arrived and promised us a magnificent bull from Normandy who would within a year fertilize all the cows who, in turn, would produce beautiful big calves. The years pass by—no bull, only letters. Then, all of a sudden, a telegram announcing the bull.

"The beaming prefect himself came to present this truly huge and powerful animal to my people. Everybody is happy, everyone rejoices in the certainty that the bad old days are gone. Tam-tams are beaten, the young people dance through the night. Next morning, the bull is ceremoniously presented with the most beautiful cows from our herd. He does not budge—only lifts his head in disdain. More cows are brought. The bull does not move. The day goes by. At night, the medicine man, who understands the language of animals, approaches the bull and asks him, 'Why do our cows not find grace in thine eyes?' And the bull replies in a sonorous deep voice, 'Monkey, don't you know I am a technical adviser?'

"You see," concluded Hajj Umar, "taking a census of our herd is a bad omen. Last time it was done, during the war, soldiers came and took away most of our livestock, explaining that we owed the government huge taxes in arrears. They took our cattle and our young and healthy sons to the army—never to be seen again. And then they promised us a prize bull, who turned out to be a technical adviser. You see, Your Excellency, for that reason my people believe that a count of our livestock is the beginning of very, very bad luck—maybe even of a new world war."

"Following this conversation, I came to the conclusion that the odds were against us, and I decided to ship my team back home as soon as possible," concluded the Ambassador in his humorous way, amidst his smiling colleagues.

An elderly, bespectacled African wearing European dress has quietly joined the little group and, with eyes fixed intensely on the ground, has heard most of the story and the others' jocular comments. He looks at the glass in his hand, takes a sip, then glances briefly at the speaker, his eyes expressing mixed anger and doubt, and silently turns about and walks across the terrace into the garden. For Dr. Kane, this is the beginning of a spoiled evening. Why, he asks himself again, why on earth do I come to these confounded uncomfortable gatherings? What am I looking for? Is it a pure case of African masochism, of wishing to be humiliated and offended by cynical, simple-minded Toubibs who are incapable of understanding their own ignorance of all things African? Why did I not respond on the spot, explain and exhort and make them aware of their ignorance? Was I afraid of a social affront? Of being considered a bad sport, an oversensitive nationalist? Or is it simply a case of an old colonial administrator lacking civic courage? By now Dr. Kane is more annoyed with himself than with the others.

In fact, he is one of the few true African intellectuals. Making the long and tortuous journey from his far-away village through mission school and high school, he completed his veterinary studies thirty years ago, at a time when the colonial master explicitly forbade the study of medicine to any native African. He studied in Europe for five years and then served the colonial government for twenty-five years as provincial chief veterinary officer all over West and Central Africa. During these lonely, difficult, and eremitic years, Dr. Kane jotted down the animal fables and legends of the different tribes among whom he worked. To his own astonishment, he became first fascinated and then deeply moved by the variegated and unknown wealth and profoundly humane wisdom of his people's oral tradition. He was surprised further when a French editor encouraged him to publish his collection, and when little by little it became accepted as a basic manual on African folklore.

When independence came overnight he made no effort to join the new government, many of whose members were his juniors. He had a feeling of foreboding and anxiety and cherished his personal freedom too much to risk compromising it at this late stage in his life. His intellectual and personal independence was soon interpreted as a subtle kind of opposition to the President and his administration. He knew and was well aware of his delicate situation and its obvious dangers. But is not age often accompanied by stubbornness?

Dr. Kane sits down heavily in one of the white garden chairs and looks westward into the ever-grandiose tropical sunset. The whole sky is aflame with deepening colors of purple and violet, mauve and endless variations of blue and yellow. He suddenly remembers a poignant myth he once heard from the fishermen in the south about the beauty of the African sunset over the Atlantic. "The Goddess of the Waters, the beautiful Yemenja, once fervently loved a human called Konuko, who was ambushed and killed at sunset by the jealous and powerful God of the Forests. In his memory, the mourning Goddess every evening paints the sky the colors of her sorrow—an eternal gift to the human race who gave her knowledge of true love and devotion."

A quiet voice speaking the African vernacular dialect of the region asks permission to join him. The newcomer is a high civil servant in the Ministry of Agriculture, about thirty years old, lanky, wearing glasses, and rather elegantly overdressed. He looks ambitious, and was once well-known for the radical leftist views he held during his student years at the agricultural university at Toulouse. He deferentially inquires about the health of the older man's family, who follows the ritual by asking the same questions in return.

After a brief silence, Dr. Kane suddenly asks, "What exactly happened to that bovine census in the north?" The younger man drinks deeply from his highball and replies with a fatalistic undertone, "You know, the usual kind of misunderstanding. The Ambassador told the President in glowing terms about the profitable modern dairy industry in his country and lamented about the heartbreaking waste here of 2 million head of cattle going from pasture to pasture, producing nothing, not even a drop of milk. . . . Well, the head of state had one of his anxious moments for our future and ordered my former minister to do something about it and to report back. Zek's first discussion with the Ambassador went extremely well, because neither he nor the Ambassador was burdened with any professional knowledge. Then the European study mission arrived with detailed plans and requested the census as a preliminary condition for carrying out the whole project. By then it was too late for Zek to retreat without losing face, but he hoped against hope for a miracle. From that moment on, he started to work really hard, so he would be transferred to the Ministry of the Interior."

Here Dr. Kane interrupts the young man. "But Zek is of Fulani origin. He knew that an imposed census would mean rebellion, driving the herds across the border, even bloodshed. Why did he agree? He is no fool!"

"Yes," replies the other, "but our capital is far from both the north and south, and, like all of us, Zek lost contact, on top of which he was under pressure to reach a compromise. He also believed that Hajj Umar would be intimidated by the President's displeasure and impressed by the police units we intended to send there. But in my opinion our real trouble is that nobody is impressed any longer by the way we handle our administration." He nodded toward the crowded and noisy living room. "They aren't, nor is Hajj Umar. If I were asked what should be done, I would have sent the army and enforced the census—bloodshed or no bloodshed. The loser in this affair is the government and all the forces of progress in this country, and that is not permissible."

Dr. Kane admits to himself that Hajj Umar's victory is a source of great satisfaction to him. He knows the old man well—one of the last great tribal kings, wise, patient, incorruptible, and truly dedicated to his people, who follow him blindly. Hajj Umar is illiterate but has more sagacity and human knowledge than these cocky, half-baked, assimilated technicians will ever acquire. The government had no right to enforce a census opposed by him and his people as long as they were convinced, albeit irrationally, that it was a maneuver preliminary to robbing them of their livestock as they had been robbed time and again over the past centuries by raiding Maures and marauding Arabs and European colonizers. Hajj Umar and his people would never believe that the white man had suddenly changed his attitude and practices overnight, as they would never believe that the President, born in the central highlands, knew their hearts and minds, their needs and wishes, better than Hajj Umar, whose family had ruled and served them for ten generations. President or ambassador or anyone else wanting to modernize the north would have to consult the Fulani and cooperate with them, winning them over by word and by deed.

They are interrupted now, by the host inquiring courteously whether all their needs are taken care of. As he moves off, the young technical adviser is hailed by an African air force officer in uniform.

Captain Koffi had been the first fighter pilot of his country and is now commander of its almost nonexistent air force. He and the young technical adviser are friends, more than friends. Both were bright children; both were taken away from their well-to-do rural families to attend schools far from home; both knew the loneliness, the despair, the pain of being separated at too tender an age from everything lovable, enjoyable, and secure; and both grew to manhood in Europe—that feared and admired Europe where all men are strangers to each other and where everyone strives to outdo everyone else.

After years of homesickness and yearning, of love and hate for their ever-new surroundings, they both returned home to discover that the Africa of their childhood memories and dreams had disappeared as if it had never been, and that the Europe of their youth was lost as well. Both had become highly competent in their professions and both were politically ambitious, and life had taught them that a good dose of cynicism is one of the best defenses in human relations.

Now they talk quietly in a corner of the garden, tense and deeply absorbed. They soon separate and walk off in different directions.

But nothing goes unnoticed at a cocktail party. Standing on the crowded terrace, Lieutenant-Colonel Dupré, a tall, haggard man with an elongated ascetic face and long whitish-blond hair, wearing a bemedalled air force uniform, has observed the two men talking in the garden. He shakes his head, shrugs his shoulders, and murmurs to himself, *"Encore un autre,"* finishes his highball in one large gulp and walks with a pronounced limp toward the waiter bearing drinks. Lieutenant-Colonel Dupré is deeply distressed and preoccupied with troubles of his own making.

Dupré's interest in life has always been airplanes. He had been a pilot well-known for his courage and daring until a crash some years ago forced him into a teaching position at the air force academy, where he met the young African student Koffi. The two men soon became friends, notwithstanding the differences in age and background. Dupré helped Koffi with his studies and was rewarded with the young man's unfailing friendship. He liked Koffi's dedication, his courage and singlemindedness, and his sense of mission for his newly independent country.

Years later, when Dupré was suddenly requested to assist as

air attaché in the setting up of the air force in Koffi's country, he realized that Koffi had singlehandedly engineered his transfer and promotion. He left for Africa with a zeal and sense of dedication that surprised even himself, eagerly looking forward to the creation of an air force that would do honor to himself and to Koffi—a crowning of his career. Yes, he came to Africa like an eager second lieutenant to his first command—full of illusions and naïve goodwill.

Here he had met with complications and unending troubles. Apportioned budgets never actually came through, recruiting had to stop, the aging and unsuitable airplanes that were supplied were often not fit to fly any longer. There were never enough spare parts and equipment to keep the two old transport planes airworthy, his handful of pilots flying, and the ground crews busy. But on a national holiday, with its splendid military parade, spare parts were suddenly plentiful, budgets unfroze, and even the Minister of the Armed Forces showed interest in the sorry state of the air force. After the parade, the interest evaporated as quickly as African spring rain, and everything returned to static somnolence.

During Dupré's two years in Africa, Koffi had been a constant friend and companion, sharing the woes and frustrations in making the air force progress, even if at a snail's pace, against all official odds. Dupré surmised that Koffi felt much worse about the situation than he did himself. After all, this was Koffi's country, and Koffi had nowhere else to turn or go back to. And he knew that Koffi had been cheated and tricked by his superiors and by his government—a government that never kept its promises, that confounded words with deeds, deceiving its people with verbosities that were never acted on, a government of so-called politicians who mistook their own petty personal ambitions and antipathies for politics, a government that produced games (if anything) but never bread for its impoverished, illiterate, and sick population.

Suddenly, like lightning out of a blue sky, one evening a week ago Koffi had asked Dupré whether he would be prepared to act as an expert and kind of liaison between his military mission and a group of army conspirators—if and when the latter were ready to seize power. Dupré had refused on the spot. The incident created a most uncomfortable dilemma. Dupré's military background, the position in Africa he was entrusted with, his own natural understanding demanded that he report at once to his superiors at the embassy on the projected military coup. But here was this fool Koffi—a fellow officer, an old friend, a dedicated, unselfish leader of men formed partly by himself and having worked with him for years. . . . How could he have him thrown into prison, expose him to torture, perhaps even to the firing squad? Dupré himself had no fond feelings for the government—for that matter, he had none for his own back home, which kept this African one in power by providing it piecemeal with financial and technical assistance. *What* should he do? Report Koffi and live forever after with the knowledge of having betrayed a friend? Keep quiet and, without wanting to, become part of a conspiracy, with all its personal dangers and with all its dishonor? Dupré did not know what to do, how to react. He took to drinking more and was seen less in his military circles. This evening, he is a man alone.

The Soviet Ambassador goes from group to group, shaking hands and talking of the weather, water skiing, and social events of no consequence. He is a man of medium height, looking younger than his age. The long straw-blond hair falling over his wide, smiling face contrasts strangely with his cold blue eyes. He drinks sparingly and feels exceedingly hot and uncomfortable, but he is happy and well-satisfied. Africa has been good to him. He is now on the last leg of his tour here and expects to be recalled soon, and he has reason to believe that his new assignment will take him to a key nation in the Near East—a surprising nomination, indeed, since the post is generally reserved for more experienced senior diplomats.

When he arrived in this part of Africa as one of the very first Soviet diplomats, the going was hard. African animosity to all things pertaining to the Soviet Union—its policies, its culture, and its ideology—was almost hysterical. The colonialists had sown the seeds of distrust and hostility very deep. But with time and the right attitude, things had changed. He cultivated the friendship of the important Western ambassadors, he gave the largest and most lavish social parties in the capital, he never discussed international or African politics or personalities in public. He had successfully brought the cultural and intellectual life of the Soviet Union to the attention of the African elite. He had arranged invitations for many dozens of African notables to go to the Soviet Union, and they returned full of praise for what they had been shown. He chose his country's best documentary films on cultural topics and quietly arranged their showing all over the country. The administration and the elite were impressed by his seriousness and dedication.

Meanwhile the world situation had changed, too. Coexistence was no longer a mere catchword. To him its first and foremost consequence was his emancipation, his full acceptance into the social and diplomatic life of the capital, and the recognition that he represented a world power. Carefully, his mission began to branch out into formerly delicate sectors. Labor leaders were invited to attend congresses in Eastern Europe, student leaders and youth groups toured the Soviet Union. The year before, he had crowned his African career with a most important assistance project, the establishment of a tuna-fishing and canning complex requiring a Soviet investment of nearly $6 million. Negotiations had been slow and arduous but had finally led to an agreement. At the same time—and the Ambassador had strongly insisted on perfect timing—a cultural, educational and information accord was officially concluded, for the first time allowing some real elbow room for political action in that part of Africa. He would leave an important heritage; the groundwork was done.

The Japanese chargé d'affaires, who is present among the guests, had only this morning drawn his government's attention to some peculiar facts concerning this "fishing and canning complex." Some ten years ago, he reminded his department, an international organization's special mission made a detailed but little known piscicultural and oceanographic study of these African shores. The study had concluded that the local tuna could not be relied on to justify the establishment of local canning industry, because its migratory routes led to this part of the African coast only every three or four years. The reason for an irregularity of more than a thousand kilometers in the tuna's migratory pattern was yet unknown to science, but the profitability of any project based on an offshore fishing-vessel fleet and a large canning plant located on the shore was highly questionable. Something seemed economically very unsound, almost hazardous, in the Soviet commitment. But there was no doubt in the chargé's mind about its political implications and its advantages for Moscow.

The chargé looks across the lawn at the Soviet Ambassador and smiles to himself. "This man is lucky, but his successor is not to be envied."

A few paces away, in the middle of the lawn, the United States Ambassador puts his arm around the shoulders of the Minister of Agriculture and takes him aside to the empty chairs under the gum tree. The Ambassador does not speak French and the Minister does not understand English, so the American councillor loudly and nervously translates back and forth. The Ambassador's problem is not a serious one—in fact it is rather funny—but this morning he has received a cabled inquiry from the undersecretary in Washington requesting an immediate report.

The facts, he explains to the Minister of Agriculture (who knows them well but acts as though he were hearing them for the first time) are simple. Some eighteen months ago, the previous Minister of Agriculture asked for an American gift of 35 jeeps in order to motorize his agricultural extension service—thereby rendering effective agricultural supervision possible even during the rainy season in the more remote parts of the country. The Ambassador, seconded by the chief of his aid mission, had warmly recommended the gift project to Washington and after some wrangling over technical matters obtained approval for it. In his opinion, the project was geared to increased agricultural efficiency, was relatively simple and inexpensive, and could easily be publicized both in Africa and back home. One beautiful day five months back, a ship entered harbor carrying the 35 jeeps. The following day a truly impressive ceremony took place at the pier. The shiny new vehicles were lined up in front of a white harbor shed, and a small stand was erected in front of them, covered with a red carpet, with a microphone in the center. At 10 o'clock sharp, dozens and dozens of limousines poured in. The Minister of Agriculture and most of his higher-echelon staff, the press, film crews, recording teams, a detachment of the National Guard clad in bright red uniforms and presenting arms, most of the diplomatic corps (informed at the last moment)—everybody of any importance was present. Seven speeches were made: the Ambassador, handing over the cars—in English; the Minister of Agriculture, accepting them with gratitude and feelings of deep friendship—in French; the head of the U.S. aid mission, describing in detail how an efficient extension service should be run—again in English; the director of the extension services, putting his excellent French to the task of describing how these cars would, under the guidance of the President and with the plans of the Minister, carry the agricultural revolution into the farthest corners of the country; three other Africans unknown to the Ambassador, thanking him in French for his understanding of the country's needs, praising this historic occasion as a milestone in international cooperation.

All in all, the two-hour ceremony was one of the most satisfying and gratifying moments of the Ambassador's African career. For days the newspapers wrote of the event, and for weeks all moviegoers appreciated the festive occasion in picture and sound.

Three months passed, and all this was forgotten—until one day a letter arrived at the embassy from the director of customs, demanding immediate payment of $235,000 customs duties in arrears, plus storage fees, for station wagons of the jeep type. The director of customs quoted the relevant paragraph of the Customs and Port Regulations stating that if arrears were not paid within fifteen days of receipt of the letter he, the director of customs, would be compelled by law to put the cars on auction and sell them to the highest bidder.

At first the Ambassador decided to treat the matter with diplomatic hauteur. He sent a second secretary with a request for an explanation. But when he realized that *his* 35 station wagons were still standing in front of the harbor shed on flat tires, already somewhat rusty, windows partly broken, spare tires, windshield wipers, and removable equipment stolen, he flew into a rage.

The President received him with the utmost courtesy. Everybody regretted the incident and promised to do everything possible to help. But no one could tell him exactly where things had gone wrong. Legally, the cars were shipped to and destined for the embassy. As they were not intended for diplomatic use but for local consumption, the 120% customs duty on American cars, and of course the storage fees as well, had to be paid by someone. Everybody agreed that the customs regulations did not intelligently cover the special case under review—a gift from one government to another and not a commercial transaction. But the Ambassador surely understood that while the customs law can be defective, the Law is the Law, and it must be respected, especially in developing countries. . . .

This the Ambassador absolutely refused to do, and he now heatedly explains to the new Minister of Agriculture, sitting straight and tense in his white garden chair, emphasizing each sentence with an appropriate gesture. "It would seem that some of your administrative services openly support the monopoly of the French car industry in this country and are preventing the importation of vehicles from any other country, even to the detriment of your own economy and development plans, and are ready to sabotage a government-to-government gift project. Sir, I'm afraid I must tell you quite frankly . . ."

The bored Minister lifts his arm and turns his head to the councillor, sitting nervously on the edge of his chair. "Please tell His Excellency that I am prepared to give him personal and confidential advice on this regrettable incident—but only if he undertakes, upon his honor, to keep our conversation confidential in the strictest sense. I want no repeating and no reporting of this! Is this clear and accepted?" The Minister turns back, his eyes on the Ambassador, and extends his right hand. The Ambassador has no choice but to shake it.

"Please explain to His Excellency that our head of state received the Mexican Ambassador today, and they put the finishing touches to plans for an official visit our President will make to Mexico. He will inaugurate our pavilion at the international fair; then there will be honorary doctorates, addresses to Parliament and the Senate, and a few lectures. I know that he would be most favorably impressed if you, Mr. Ambassador, were to invite him to pay an official visit—it is clear that it should be an official one—to your own country. May I suggest that, as you extend this invitation to our President, you should indicate, as delicately as possible, that the jeep incident, unimportant as it may seem, could nevertheless create some intangible psychological difficulties; it would seem ever so much wiser to do away with this matter before his visit to your country is actively considered and planned. In my opinion, our head of state will understand immediately and, for the sake of our future even more excellent relations, will do all he can to help you solve this annoying problem. Again, I want His Excellency to know that I count upon his discretion."

The Minister rises and with a broad smile on his handsome face shakes hands again with the Ambassador and the councillor. Assembling his assistants around him, he walks over to his host to shake hands and take his leave. On his way out he turns to his chef de cabinet, a cousin and his only confidant, and whispers in the southern dialect, "Remind me to phone the President about my conversation." He chuckles. "Oh, these simple-minded Anglo-Saxons!"

Meanwhile the Ambassador, still sitting in the garden, is thinking furiously. How will the Department react to a sudden proposal of an official visit? What will the President's timetable be in September? Can he fit another African head of state into his schedule? And this African visitor—where will he appear and speak? What are his opinions on the Vietnam war and the race problem in the States? Here the Ambassador's brow clears some-what. The African President is known for his moderate evolu-tionary views—most definitely welcome to the American adminis-tration at this juncture. He rises with a sigh of relief. "For a change, the party has been worth while," he thinks, glancing at his watch and starting to look around for his host.

The party has dwindled down to a few dozen people, dispersed in groups of twos and threes in the dark and spacious drawing room, on the wide terrace, and in the garden, now lit with numerous small colored electric lights strung among the trees. The remain-ing guests are of two types: those who enjoy a free drink and those engrossed in conversation. There are very few Africans, but in a corner of the still hot drawing room one is seated with a Euro-pean at a low table. The conversation is animated.

Dr. Madenga teaches first- and second-year students at the cap-ital's medical school—one of Africa's few professors who had found his way back to the continent of his birth. He married a French girl, a former student, and by now they have four chil-dren—sensitive, intelligent, and quick-witted. They are a close-knit and apparently happy family, but at first their problems were enormous. His wife's relatives, scandalized by the marriage, had refused to receive him, she was ostracized by her former friends, and he was stigmatized by his African compatriots for being a "white negro," one who wanted to forget the color of his skin. As time went by, feelings abated; his in-laws felt irresistibly attracted to their grandchildren and even to him. The Madengas found a new circle of friends and social acquaintances. Then, prodded by his wife, he accepted his first teaching appointment in Africa. But Dr. Madenga was an intelligent man; he chose never to return to his own family in Dahomey, never to expose his wife and children to local African prejudice, believing they were not strong enough, and perhaps too spoiled, to face such an experience. He now lived in Africa among people of his own color—and yet as a stranger. He was an African expatriate in their midst, accepted because he was needed; but, he knew, the day might not be far off when a young local specialist would take his place for no other reason than that he was the "local" man and Madenga the "African stranger." Talking frankly once with very close friends, he remarked laughingly that he was the original African Jew. Dr. Madenga never relinquished his French passport, remained active in metropolitan medical affairs, and continued to cultivate his many European professional acquaintances.

The European seated across the table is but a chance acquaintance. He is the head of the aid mission of a powerful and wealthy Central European state, an engineer and economist by training, holding his first African post. His country has of late shown a burst of good will toward developing nations, motivated by an historic urge to change its somber international image and to blot out the memory of a grim past. The Ambassador, skillfully putting these winds of change to use, initiated a most ambitious assistance scheme, which later was ceremoniously requested by the African head of state himself during an official visit to the Ambassador's country. Agreements were signed, studies and plans were submitted, and within two years a most impressive modern hospital saw the light of day. Roads were laid, air-conditioned buildings were constructed and equipped with the most up-to-date medical and surgical installations. The hospital boasted of three fully-equipped operating theaters, its own electric generator, an automated laundry, an electric kitchen—in short, at the cost of some $3 million, it was the last word in medical science, a marvel of modern European technology, something very few countries could boast of.

The hospital was situated in a densely populated rural area in the center of the country's most fertile region, some 300 kilometers east of the capital—a region with a high rate of illiteracy, ravaged by seasonal epidemics, and with a particularly distressing infant mortality rate of 60 per cent at birth. For that reason the 50-room, 300-bed hospital was conceived first and foremost as a central regional maternity station. As set forth in the agreement, a team of three physicians—two gynecologists and one general surgeon—and two head nurses came from abroad to ensure that the hospital would function well and smoothly, and to acquaint the local staff with the intricacies of the modern machinery.

It was at this point that the trouble started. No local staff could be found—neither doctors nor nurses, not even cooks, electricians, and plumbers. The Ambassador was flabbergasted, and the head of his aid mission spent weeks at the Ministry of Public Health, meeting the Minister every other day, quoting by heart Paragraph II of the agreement, which clearly stipulated the local government's responsibility for staffing the hospital with professional and technical teams. The hospital's inauguration date drew near but had to be indefinitely postponed. The European nation's Foreign Minister canceled his African tour. The ceremony, heralded as a milestone in his country's new policy, a means to win the friendship of independent African nations, and a well-advertised example of his personal effort "to turn a page and forget the past," never took place. Three months have now passed—and still no staff and still no inauguration.

The head of the aid mission, in his exact, clipped, but unspirited French, has now explained in detail to Dr. Madenga the long, sad story and is impatiently waiting for his African listener's reply. But Dr. Madenga is keeping silent. With diplomats, you never know why or how your most straightforward opinions may be distorted and used against you for being "detrimental to the best interests of the state." Madenga must be careful not to fall into a trap. What can he say without exposing himself, the medical school, or his ambiguous relations with the Minister of Health? Anyway, how can his opinion on this scandalously shameful subject be of any help? Was the diplomat perhaps playing some hidden game? Yet here is this wonderful modern hospital lying idle in the midst of misery, pain, and death. He suddenly, perhaps irrationally, feels moved to say something of the truth.

"Sir," he begins, "first of all I don't know whose medical opinion you sought or whose counsel you accepted before you decided to put your hospital out there in the middle of a medical nowhere. You know that this country has three general hospitals for four-and-a-half million inhabitants—one still run by the French Army, one by our university, which is a French Government institution, and one by our government—and you know that they are all located here in this city of 750,000 souls. Most physicians are Europeans or Americans paid by one or another assistance fund, the head nurses are nuns, and the African nurses were trained mostly in mission nursing schools. Most of them leave their profession when they marry; those who stay on are excellent but they are very few. You know that, in a Muslim society like ours, the young unmarried men and women wanting to become doctors and nurses face great social and religious pressures. But these pressures are not so great here in the capital, or at least there are compensations. Religious, or tribal, or interracial problems are not so acute. Everyone can find a social group to his liking, and everyone can advance professionally because the center of our administration also is here. The doctors get married, their children go to good schools, the nurses can prepare for an additional degree, they have the laboratories and the central library. . . . But all of this was known to you beforehand.

"We are in dire need of your maternity hospital, but you put it in the wrong place. Have you ever visited the maternity ward of the university hospital? It is hopelessly outdated, underequipped, and overcrowded. Even the corridors are used as additional wards. Conditions for surgery are so primitive and inadequate that I had better refrain from going into detail. . . . But, as a part of the university, it is still entirely financed by France to the tune of some $14 million a year, which must support five faculties with more than 400 professors and teachers for the education of less than 3,000 students. For this, we are very grateful even if our medical institutions are outdated."

Dr. Madenga stops briefly, then goes on. "There can be no rational doubt that your hospital should have been incorporated into our hospital as its maternity wing. . . . This was not done—let us again be frank—for two reasons. One, our French friends have a very pronounced sense of ownership and prestige, and it would have been something close to *lèse majesté* to build this up-to-date hospital and staff it with your people, trained in a different medical and pharmacological tradition, within a purely French institution. On the other hand, would your own government have agreed to make this huge financial contribution anonymously and simply hand over $3 million, or the hospital to our university, thereby indirectly but most effectively assisting the French Government to discharge its responsibilities? You know as well as I do that this would have been unthinkable. National prestige and interest are predominant factors in the distribution of aid to underdeveloped countries."

He pauses again, drinks deeply, and continues. "In cases like this, our African governments are actually left without a choice. If we do not agree with your conditions for setting up a bilateral project, you could easily withdraw your offer of assistance and our country would lose a great economic and social opportunity, which does not often present itself. African governments have a national obligation to attract as many aid and assistance projects as possible. The injection of foreign capital through schemes of this kind is by itself a major boost to our economy even if the project itself is problematic and questionable on professional grounds." Dr. Madenga stops and thoughtfully puts his fingertips together.

"I think there is another factor you may have overlooked. You built your hospital in a rural area settled almost exclusively by people belonging to the Tidjaniyya brotherhood. Our Muslim sects are not only fanatically religious; they are socially closed to outsiders. Even an African who is not of their creed is considered a heretic. An African physician living in that region will experience much loneliness and ostracism amidst an unsympathetic or even hostile population. Can you really expect him to live and work there for the same salary he is offered in the capital? No, I am not surprised that our administration and your embassy encounter recruiting difficulties.

"The only advice I can offer is: forget our promise to staff the hospital. Bring a complete medical and nursing staff from your country and run the hospital for, say, eight or ten years. Send the brightest and most promising youngsters from our regional high

schools to your medical schools, open a nurses' training center attached to the hospital, and pay your local staff well. You will see
how fast things will change for the better.

"Oh yes," he acknowledges a gesture from his European listener, "I understand your difficulties. No government wants to
underwrite such long-term obligations and invest so much more
than it intended. But I'm afraid it's your only choice; one has to
adapt even the most meticulous planning to realities. I do not intend to defend our Ministry of Health. According to the statistics,
we have many doctors and nurses, but the ones studying in the
United States or Europe seldom come back and those studying
here are too few to make a difference. Each year we lose a number of physicians who turn politician, administrator, or diplomat
to the government. The lot of an African doctor is difficult and
disappointing, really, because a poor population cannot compen-
sate him adequately. Professionally it is very hard to broaden
one's medical knowledge, cut off as one is from the scientific centers and being without adequate research facilities and laboratories
of one's own. One feels on the margin of the arena where professional ideas and experiences are exchanged.

"But all of this is of secondary importance," and here Dr. Madenga's voice rises. He becomes emotional and pleading as he goes
on, with great inner agitation, "Please, do not give up your hospital. Your country is rich in wealth and knowledge. You can
certainly find ways to save this project from oblivion."

Suddenly Dr. Madenga looks tired. He laughs nervously and
rises from his chair. "I believe we are among the stragglers. I will
have to leave."

The head of the aid mission is distressed. He shakes his
head pensively and murmurs his thanks to Dr. Madenga. To himself he says, "Oh, God, another intellectual visionary. He does
not understand the cold realities of these issues. Commitments and
agreements between nations are not child's play. We negotiated,
we signed an agreement with a sovereign government, we kept
our part of the deal. Why should we let the Africans get away
with this—as though our agreement was not worth the paper it is

written on? A ten-year obligation indeed! It is not only impossible, it is positively ludicrous! After all, we are not missionaries interested in saving souls. Our interests are immediate, political, economic."

No, his long conversation with the inspired, excited Dr. Madenga has been a complete failure, a waste of time. He is exhausted. He sighs, wipes the perspiration off his face and neck, and makes for the door, where the Ambassador and his entourage are shaking hands with the last guests. It is already dark, the streets are unlit; he has to let his eyesight adjust to the night, as he tries to remember where he parked his car and proceeds carefully in that direction.

The Ambassador is now alone with his two guests of honor. He is dead tired, his feet are aching, his shirt is glued to his back, he is thirsty and hungry. Tomorrow will be another long and tiring day. He walks to the terrace with his guests, sits down heavily in an armchair, and orders cold beer and sandwiches. Around them his servants are busily cleaning up. "A very successful party," he says. "Everyone seemed to have had a good time. But it is hard on the feet . . . and cocktails are a barbaric custom in this climate."

While he accompanies them to their car, his guests make courteous and tired remarks and comment favorably about some of the guests, effusively thanking the Ambassador for his efforts. Tomorrow's schedule is heavy, and the starry African night is already well advanced.

The Ambassador is content with his party. The attendance was above expectations and the service excellent. But isn't he deceiving himself? Besides receiving diplomats from more than twenty countries, he had been host to a minister, a general, an archbishop, doctors, judges, officers, professors, businessmen, and teachers representing the ruling class of an important African nation, a representative cross-section of a power elite typical of modern Africa. But what did these people actually represent? Did not their fluent French or English, their education, their professional activity, their behavioral pattern mark them as an exclusive caste, a small group trying to bridge an amorphous African past with a still uncertain future? A caste of men and women uprooted from their native soil and raised on European concepts? Their historic importance was unquestionable: they were the pioneers of the African social order yet to come. But what did they represent today and tomorrow? On whose behalf did they speak? Were they *really* representative of the natural power structure? Or did they rule by proxy for social forces that were invisible to Western eyes?

In fact, the Ambassador knows, the African ruling class is not trusted by anyone. To Westerners it falls far short of established standards. And it certainly does not represent to Africans the natural elite on whom power is bestowed by tradition, wealth, or religious hierarchy. The African intelligentsia and ruling caste run the administration, the police, the schools, the courts—in short, the West's varnish on African life. But their hold on the population is ineffective and superficial; in reality, their authority is a fact only if and when the old tribal ruling class consents to support their activities or at least agrees to compromise with their policies. In cases of disagreement between a government and the tribal ruling aristocracy, nothing can be accomplished; the wheels of government stand still.

Who, then, are the others, those millions of Africans who were not truly represented at this evening's party? Those Africans he does not even know, either personally or by their names; Africans who speak no European language. Their customs and habits are as strange to him as his to them. They do not wear European dress and are unfamiliar with his social ambiance. They would feel awkward and out-of-place and uncomfortable at his cocktail party. Who are they? The dynastic leaders of the tribes; the all-powerful city and village elders; the marabouts, the absolute, divine rulers of the numerous and mighty Muslim sects; the imams of the country's great mosques; the clan and family elders and their animistic priests and medicine-men; and last but not least, the griots, the highly appreciated wandering troubadours, the safe-keepers of the people's oral tradition and history.

All these are far away, and they are mostly unknown to Western minds and eyes, although unobtrusively their presence is felt —with the melancholic sound of the tam-tam, in the people's beliefs and devotion, by their habits and unchanging customs. They represent the continuity and the permanency of African culture and civilization; they are rooted in the African soil like a huge baobab tree; they represent Africa in its natural condition. Human conditions are of course subject to change—no civilization is static —but are Western definitions and concepts of time applicable here? Does not time, like life itself, have a different meaning in traditional Africa?

The Ambassador checks his train of thought and looks at his watch. During his years of service in Africa, he has made an unwavering habit of jotting down in his personal diary, every night before retiring, his observations, ideas, and conclusions about the day's events—and he finds much intellectual relief from the uncertainties, hesitations, and pressures of his profession in the act of keeping his diary up to date. This had been a long and interesting day, but he is exhausted. The diary will have to wait until tomorrow.

The Ambassador checks all the windows and doors. Each one is securely locked. He sees the night watchman slowly patrolling in the garden. He turns off the last lights still burning in the house and switches on the strong outdoor spotlights. Only in the garden will the lights burn throughout the night.

TWO

The
Working
Session

A

T 10 O'CLOCK THE AMBASSADOR'S CAR
stops before the Administration Building in the center of town.
The policemen on guard jump to attention, saluting smartly as a
young official of the Ministry of Agriculture ushers the Ambassador and his study mission into the main entrance of the huge,
neglected, ugly building.

All the governmental ministries are located here, the larger ones
occupying an entire floor. At all hours of the day, hundreds of
Africans clutter the staircases and sit in long, silent rows on hard
benches in the endless corridors, waiting to be taken care of or
spoken to. Some are office-seekers, others come from the interior
looking for a relative, a job, a loan, a meal, a place to stay overnight. Others are civil servants from the provinces coming to be
heard, to complain, to obtain promised funds, transfers, promo-
tions. The administrations of all developing countries are path-
ologically swollen and deformed. The government is not only the
main economic initiator and investor but also the only employer

of importance. All those who wish to leave the provinces, who need a job, drift quite naturally to a relative, a friend, a tribal connection in government service. There is practically no other place to turn to.

The Ambassador and his suite are shown into the Director General's spacious office. A large air-conditioner is humming monotonously. The tall, distinguished African, a middle-aged agronomist trained in France, courteously offers seats to his guests. His European councillor enters discreetly, files in hand. The meeting can begin.

The first item on the agenda is the poultry project, which by now has been functioning for well over three years, apparently with great success. It has had three basic objectives: to stop the drain on the country's financial resources caused by the importation, mostly by air, of some 18 million eggs a year from Europe; to provide an additional source of income for the country's poorer farmers; and to create a local source of comparatively inexpensive animal protein. For a people permanently suffering from malnutrition the poultry project is of great economic and social importance. An experimental avicultural station was built, selected poultry were flown in, two incubators were set up, chicks were scientifically bred, raised, and then sold at cost to the farmers. A rudimentary extension service supervised the growing flocks of white poultry.

In conformity with the plan, the government was able to end the importation of eggs after three years. The investment of the donor government by now amounted to $450,000 and the project still required the presence of two European technicians. Having attained its first objective, however, the undertaking encountered unexpected difficulties—lack of suitable transportation facilities, the high price of imported chicken feed, a lack of marketing outlets, and, above all, an astonishing and unexplained overproduction: the earlier annual consumption of 18 million eggs had not been increased. How was this to be explained? Were the eggs too expensive, or did Africans simply not like eggs?

The Director General is persuasive, almost convincing. Prices will have to be lowered, chicken feed subsidized, suitable storage space erected—needless to say with the donor government's assistance and at its expense. It is clear that the sponsor country's continued participation and contribution is not only more necessary than ever but simply imperative. The Director General—a born public speaker—speaks well in his fluent and well-modulated French.

The Technical Mission's agronomist, making use of his colorless high school French and searching here and there for the right word, resents his own linguistic inferiority, but he makes his point. His government has already doubled the financial contribution contemplated in the original agreement. The project has now reached maturity and should, in a year, pass into the hands of the local administration—one year behind schedule. This additional year will be added at the donor government's expense to ensure the efficiency of the avicultural station's technical staff, particularly its extension services. Then everything will be ready for the complete take-over of the project by the Ministry of Agriculture.

The conversation goes on and on. The Ambassador does not intervene. For some time now, he has realized that the difficulties of the poultry project were not entirely of a technical or financial nature. At the planning stage, he had enthusiastically sponsored the project, believing it not only politically advantageous but also technically sound, easy to implement, and of a truly progressive social character, and therefore kept himself informed of its progress. When the problem of overproduction arose, he tried, in his quiet deductive way, to find a practical solution. Speaking with the African headmaster of a boarding school about the possibility of serving the pupils one egg daily, he received an evasive reply. Discussing the same matter, an elderly army officer in charge of kitchen and canteen supplies, whom he met by chance, laughed heartily, white teeth flashing in his broad face, and explained that African soldiers did not like eggs and that most of them would simply refuse them. Undoubtedly, their motives were based on some regrettable superstition—mass superstition is always a nuisance for a supply officer, like Muslims and Jews not eating pork.

Africans in these regions believed that pregnant women who ate eggs would bear deaf-mute children; generally speaking, no African would choose to eat eggs for fear of their potential ill effects upon his offspring and even upon his virility. "These are very old and deeply-rooted beliefs which are not easy to eradicate," the officer added. At first the Ambassador was not convinced, but he pursued his quiet campaign until no further doubt was possible. Even his sophisticated African friends, educated in Europe, did their best to avoid eggs—one on the pretext of a delicate liver, another because of a very complicated diet, and so on. Never did they mention that tradition, taboos, or superstition might lie at the root of their gastronomic customs—an unthinkable admission. Rigid social convention prohibits the African from touching upon a subject concerning typically African behavior that differs from the European pattern. The African has learned the bitter historic lesson that in European eyes, anything different is primitive, ludicrous, even despicable.

His inquiries led the Ambassador to the conclusion that eggs in Africa were quite a different matter from eggs in Europe. He did not convey this information to his avicultural technicians or his Foreign Ministry; this would have served no good purpose. After all, the project had its positive aspects: it furnished an additional income to farmers; it provided fresh eggs for the tables of the numerous European and Lebanese families living in the cities; and it freed the local exchequer from the strain of an unnecessary import. His authorities wouldn't understand the problem anyhow, and some simpleton might even misconstrue the situation and create a controversial issue involving his personal standing and responsibility in the matter. Nobody wants to be a scapegoat. The Ambassador did not intervene. But he is quite happy that the project will soon be officially concluded and taken off the list of his responsibilities.

Another item on the agenda is tackled. Amidst great expectations and much publicity, an ambitious settlement scheme had been started two years ago to reclaim lands in the southeastern part of the country. The reclamation project was financed and carried out by a very efficient international development agency specializing in this field, and the Ambassador's government had undertaken to assist on a bilateral basis in its agricultural and social implementation. Detailed plans for a modern regional settlement scheme of eighteen new villages and one central town were worked out in detail. The considerable investment in construction, access roads, basic agricultural equipment, drilled wells, irrigation canals, and power and pumping stations offered a rare opportunity to lead African agriculture straight from the subsistence-level age into the modern industrial marketing era. It seemed to be a risk well worth taking. The agricultural economy of the new region was to be based on the exploitation of intensively irrigated sugar cane, sorghum, corn and rice fields. In the town intended as the economic and social center for the entire region, food-processing industries were to be established. The town would also be endowed with two schools, a hospital, and two social centers (to be erected at different stages). In short a revolutionary, most attractive, and very costly conception of things to come.

The first two villages were built and formally inaugurated by the head of state. Young men and women were carefully screened, put through special agricultural training courses, screened again after a year, and the most promising among them were settled in the new villages. The cotton, rice, sorghum, and sugar cane fields were placed under the strict supervision of European experts, and a European social worker looked after the social and human aspects of the new communities.

The preparatory courses continued and another model village was now under construction. But the financing of this important project became more burdensome as unforeseen expenses grew. International and inter-European organizations are easily induced to initiate projects, and they proudly claim their paternity; but they are not much interested in cooperating with other partners to see the schemes through the difficult development stages to fruition. Marketing difficulties not anticipated in the detailed plans plagued the project; out of the arid zone, insects and birds suddenly appeared by the millions and devastated the crops, and new means of protection had to be devised; rentability never reached envisaged standards.

But the worst complication of all could not have been foretold in the most conscientious plans of the most renowned agronomists, rural architects, and economists. Relations between the European experts and their African counterparts and the settlers grew tense. Not a day went by without incidents of one kind or another, and after a few months many of the young settler families disappeared overnight and returned to their former villages. The reasons they gave were many: fathers were old and sick and mothers were expecting, brothers were moving to the city and sisters had to be married. But meanwhile, after two years of effort, the settler population was still unstable, its social organization was unreliable, and agricultural production was directly affected.

The Director of the Foreign Aid and Assistance Division is now talking at length, requesting the African government to take a more direct responsibility in running and financing the villages, and informing the Director General that in one year's time, in accordance with the signed commitment, his European technicians will have to return home. The Director General does not agree: Patience and good will are necessary—another year at least of budgetary and advisory assistance ought to be added to the commitment. The Chief of the Aid Mission finally agrees to refer the matter back home. The conversation goes on without reaching any kind of effective conclusion.

The Ambassador's participation in the conversation is a formal one only. He is not sure but suspects that, just as with the egg project, the true reason for the difficulties encountered has not been revealed. The economics of the project were basically sound; he had studied them in every detail. The fault lies somewhere in the planning of the social and human aspects of the scheme, but where? Against his better judgment, he decides to ask the Director General some leading questions: "How does the new settlement scheme fit into the region's tribal structure? Why did the young settlers leave this better existence, with its secure future, to go

back to their poor and hungry villages? Why did you not foresee
that this might occur?"

The Africans are taken by surprise. They are uneasy and offended. They have been dealing with their European counterparts
on a common level of rationality—plans, figures, investment budgets, equipment, seeds, and produce. Why does the Ambassador
depart from accepted conventions? Africa needs Western aid in
agricultural technology and industrial development, yes, but certainly not interference in the problems arising from the painful
process of changing an archaic society. The white man owes
Africa a debt—a great debt incurred through slavery, colonialism,
and exploitation. But he has no right to interfere in the delicate
zone of African interrelations. That deep-seated European racist
superiority complex expresses itself in these insinuating questions.

The Director General's reply is short, sharp, and inconclusive.
Everyone returns, obviously relieved, to the figures in the file under review.

The Ambassador is not impressed; he has had long experience
with these African susceptibilities, and he regards them as a kind
of delayed defence mechanism set up against antiquated European superstitions and prejudices about the black man. Centuries
ago, these puritanical prejudices had served to justify the establishment of slavery and colonial exploitation. And the African, like
the Jew, is not capable of forgetting or forgiving. But am I, are we
responsible for the deeds of our ancestors? Are we morally bound
to repay debts they have incurred? Our technological aid, the
heavy financial responsibility we undertake, our human commitment, are they not a trustworthy sign that we are in earnest, that
we consider the African as our equal, that we want to cooperate
to the best of our capacity and knowledge in the betterment of his
lot? African and European susceptibilities are not only obsolete,
they create misunderstandings and always lead to dangerously in-
accurate evaluations. How can they be overcome?

An African technician seated to the left of the Director General
has followed the discussion with mounting interest. He is the

agricultural engineer nominally in charge of the project, and he has been living on the spot with his family for the past two years. Daily he worked with the European experts and experienced all the ups and downs with them. He was impressed and soon became infected with their dedication and singlemindedness. They became his close friends and companions. He began to grasp how their minds worked. They wanted to analyze everything, and in their terminology, the intricacies of the *African* mind made up a component, called "human material," upon which the success or failure of "their" project depended. He once tried to explain to one of them that he himself no longer understood the minds of the rural people of this district. Many years ago he would have known or found out from his uncles, aunts, half brothers, but now he is a stranger. The villages had changed in many ways: old taboos had fallen, new ones had taken their place, family ties had lost much of their former strength, European influences had made inroads; greed, social jealousies, tension between generations and age groups had appeared; easy money had become more alluring than age-old dignity. The youngsters, drifting away to the city and the army, returned home bearing corrosive doubts about the formerly unquestionable and unquestioned authority of the elders.

This—and much more—was all too complicated, too fluid and elusive to be defined in terms of planning and action! The white man was not a wise man! He could not understand the African situation. He wanted to analyze, diagnose, and evaluate in the light of his own experience and knowledge—on his own terms.

Still, the engineer feels much sympathy for the Ambassador and knows that his questions bear no malice, yet he agrees wholeheartedly with the Director General's short and cutting reply. Could the Ambassador's questions actually be answered? Would the answers help the project's chances of success? The Europeans know well that new settlement schemes in Africa are very rare —in fact, revolutionary. The African rural population, immersed in its tribal background, conceives of human society as an harmonious entity—a whole from the ancestor to the unborn babe. The social structure is rigidly organized in age groups, each having its privileges and its strict responsibilities and bound to the others by fate. No African can live alone; no age group can exist apart from its elders or juniors. A separated age group is an unbalanced, artificial phenomenon, it cannot stand on its own, and is not capable of governing itself. Yet here too the situation is not static. Many of the younger generation want to leave their villages, to break with an old and suffocating order, to move ahead and better their lives. The resettlement project offered them that chance. If they succeeded, they would become the pioneers of a modern rural society in Africa. If not, what would it prove? This Western obsession with speed—cutting the time element and linking it with concepts of money and profitability—was wrong once again. How long had it taken the European farmer to make his way to independence and affluence?

A new item is raised by the Director for Aid and Assistance: the seed distribution program initiated last year. The idea for this crash program was forced upon his government by nature itself. Two years ago, the country had suffered a prolonged drought. Sorghum, corn, rice, and cassava seedlings had dried in the fields long before harvest time, and in desperation the farmers had used their last remaining seed grains to feed their families. An acute national calamity threatened if seeds were not rushed in time for the forthcoming sowing season; prices of staple foodstuffs would skyrocket and social unrest would follow. The Western nations, for once, made a concerted effort, and some 50,000 tons of grain and seed were rushed to the affected regions as an outright gift. The Ambassador's government sent some 500 tons of high-class selected sorghum and corn seed for distribution in the south. But it was evident that large quantities of these seeds had disappeared somewhere on the way from the port to their destination. Other grains had simply been eaten up by the farmers during the "bridging period"—three foodless summer months between the sowing and the harvests.

As is so often the case in Africa, the donors are asking questions and the Africans are having to explain. It is hard to pin down responsibilities. The agricultural extension services in charge of distributing the emergency shipments were not well organized. Their on-the-spot monitors cover too large an area and are unable adequately to check and supervise the use of fertilizers, seed, or food. Their means of transportation are scarce and badly maintained. For weeks and months during the rainy season entire regions are isolated. Much material is lost, spoiled, or stolen. The monitors themselves soon become discouraged and fall prey to clannish village interests, take sides in family disputes, side with one family against another—and lose their standing and effectiveness.

The conversation becomes animated. The Director General suavely and subtly proposes a radical yet simple solution to the country's permanent difficulties in getting enough good and selected seeds: the establishment of an agricultural station for the production of selected rice, sorghum, and corn seeds. The Study Mission is vividly interested in this unexpected suggestion.

It is common knowledge to all of the men present that one of the major causes for the low yields of African crops lies in the use of defective or sterile seeds. African farmers sow their harvested grains over and over again for years and even for generations without ever selecting or renewing them. In order to ensure some success, they will then put ten or twelve seeds into one seedhole —instead of the two or three needed when the seed is of good quality. All over Africa, experimental stations have proven that even without changing his archaic agricultural techniques, the African farmer could double his yields simply by switching to selected and healthy seeds.

Here at last is an opportunity to do something tangible in an important and vital field! Notes are taken and more study missions are projected to prepare survey reports on the selected region, its meteorology, ecology, and biology in relation to its agricultural potential. The building of access roads, construction of farm buildings, selection of mechanical and irrigation equipment and many more matters will have to be researched and studied.

It is now 11:30. The Minister is waiting. He welcomes his guests at the door of his large, cool, and darkened office. He met the two members of the Study Mission at the cocktail party the evening before, and his greetings are hospitable and warm. The Minister listens to the Director General's brief summary of the work done in the past hours, and then asks to hear the Ambassador's comments on the three assistance projects discussed. After offering a few probing general questions to ascertain whether his guests' good will and readiness continue, he asks their permission to raise two additional points.

In a short speech, the Minister now requests the advice and assistance of his European friends in the arduous, very costly task of mechanizing the local agriculture. Combines are needed, in his opinion, for the rice fields in the south and the sorghum and corn fields in the north. Irrigation equipment—water pumps, mostly —is also needed in the south and near the capital. Heavy tractors for moving earth and light tractors for the fields are needed everywhere. Would the Study Mission's government be prepared to assist in the realization of such a plan?

The Study Mission and the Ambassador are taken by surprise. They are noncommittal and cautious: Are there technicians available who can run and service this new and complicated mechanical equipment? The Minister's reply is optimistic but evasive; after all, he is not professionally acquainted with the mechanics and maintenance of agricultural machinery, but the head of the department in question, a French engineer, is most positive.

The members of the Study Mission are now on the defensive. They definitely are *not* interested, but good manners and the diplomatic code prohibit a straightforward negative reply. They have seen too many machinery graveyards all over Africa to believe that such a costly investment could solve the problem of low productivity and inefficiency. Communications are too difficult, distances too great, repair facilities too spotty, the maintenance organization unreliable. The Ambassador assures the Minister that his request will be studied and most favorably considered—meaning shelved.

The Minister moves to his second topic. He is speaking now in glowing terms of the famous and venerable universities of the Ambassador's country and puts forth a request for six fellowships for graduate and postgraduate studies for members of his ministry. His country urgently needs trained and qualified staff on the M.A. and Ph.D. levels. He underlines the special need for fellowships in agricultural chemistry, soil movement and conservation, hydraulics, and genetics—their importance for the future of the nation, for Africa as a whole, is fervently and convincingly described. Has the Minister forgotten his audience? Eyes half closed, he might be addressing a rally or an international conference.

The Ambassador and the Study Mission are relieved. The Western world holds an almost religious belief in the formation of a highly trained and specialized academic elite as one of the key factors in technological progress and social evolution. Ergo, all developing nations need more and better specialists in all fields so as to promote development and ensure their own technological future. Western eagerness outdoes itself and readily backs the African thirst for knowledge and advancement. European and American universities compete for thousands of students. For the young, gifted, and ambitious African, study abroad is the fulfillment of his most cherished dreams. It opens the doors to employment in government agencies and is a stepping stone on the way to achieving social status and a career. The allocation of academic fellowships is politically very important therefore and strictly controlled by the government. Fellowships are usually granted as an acknowledgment of services rendered or as an official favor.

The subject of the graduates' future employment and usefulness is scarcely raised. After all, four to five years are a long time for personnel planning anywhere and in Africa in particular. But the Ambassador cannot share in the general exuberance. He reproaches himself for being overly critical without being able to make an accurate analysis of the matter under discussion or to put forth a positive or helpful new approach. He has to beware of being misunderstood. Nobody wants to be a hair-splitter, a perennially negative critic. Anyway, his main job is to cultivate his country's relations with this African nation, not to solve its development problems. If fellowships could serve that end, why should he not agree with the idea and simply ignore the deeper implications? If the African government—or for that matter his own—did not wish to recognize these implications and draw the conclusion, why should he resent their facile optimism?

The meeting ends at exactly five minutes to noon. The Minister rises, salutations are exchanged, hands are warmly shaken many times over, as demanded by African custom, and the visitors are quickly escorted to the exit. In a few minutes, the huge building will empty within seconds: all of Francophonic Africa goes to lunch at exactly the same moment. Usually complacent people suddenly become nervous; streets are blocked as cars go off in all directions; generally courteous men turn into impolite and aggressive drivers. Thousands of people pull and push and rush about. Fifteen minutes later, the street has returned to its normally polite, hot, humid, dusty, and passive existence.

The Ambassador's car cautiously makes its way through the heavy traffic. His colleagues are favorably impressed with this morning's working session and start to discuss their departure, scheduled for the evening, and tomorrow's stopover in a nearby African capital.

The Ambassador feels relieved at the thought that they will be leaving soon. Study missions of high officials are a waste of time and money. No one can acquaint himself in a few days or even weeks with the intricacies of modern Africa. Anyway, most of these men spend their short time in Africa listening to their representatives on the spot. Would it not be more effective, much less expensive, and more comfortable for the people back home to read our reports attentively and answer our requests promptly? But all foreign ministries want to be in direct contact with the complex realities of new nations, so the missions come and go.

Diplomats based in Africa go on being apprehensive; the risk of misunderstanding, of misjudging a given situation is considerable indeed.

The two guests are happily talking about this morning's work. They are genuinely convinced that they have helped their Ambassador enormously to streamline and promote their country's program of assistance and cooperation for this African nation, and that they have left a positive impression on their African hosts. "Everything is working out fine," thinks the Ambassador. "Good luck to my colleagues at the next stopover."

Driving slowly, the car enters the residential suburb, then Embassy Row. Lunch will be served soon.

From the Ambassador's diary:
June 12, 19..
. . . . The Study Mission has finally left—without much damage, without breaking our china. . . . Thanks for that!

The working session . . . the six graduate and postgraduate scholarships actually do present an irritating and complex problem, at least to me. There are undeniable short-term and long-term advantages in granting these fellowships: the power and strength of the cultural and linguistic ties established are permanent, influential, all-pervading. The acquisition of an academic degree is first and foremost a cultural event. The returning African, throughout his entire professional and private life, will be to a large extent the living product of the civilization that indoctrinated him. The language he learned, the profession he chose, the civilization he came to identify with have an effect beyond the single homecoming student. Friends, college students, family—they all will be marked by his European cultural and professional background.

And the short-term aspect is just as important. A physician trained in France naturally uses French pharmacopoeia, French instruments, French equipment. An engineer trained in the United States instinctively turns to American equipment and to American professional and general literature. So, any power attempting to capture a sphere of political and economic influence in the underdeveloped world must invest in the formation of its emerging elite. The effective and real zones of power in Africa today are established in the contexts of language, science and culture. In the past, continents were won by gunboats and soldiers. Now the future belongs to those who win the allegiance of the continent's new ruling elite.

What is the African's point of view? What are the motivating forces behind *his* actions?

The ties linking an African politician and intellectual to the European Metropole are primarily personal, cultural, and emotional—economic and political in the second instance only. A moderate, Francophonic African head of state shapes his country's constitution, his public image, his behavior after France and General de Gaulle. The leader of the outlawed opposition, the African Communist, draws his inspiration from the European communists. Nkrumah's influential advisors were British leftists, not Cubans or Chinese. The elite's conception of African evolution and ideology is inspired by and patterned after the Western models it knows best. Here the African feels on safe ground, here are the roots of his emotional and cultural experience.

His attitude toward other Western political and cultural centers is one of wariness and ambivalence. He tries to take advantage of all, but he lacks flexibility and confidence. His vision of the future is basically a projection of *his* European experience adapted to Black Africa.

Now obviously Europe's science and technology are the motive forces behind her power and wealth, and, if this is so, ways and means will have to be found to transfer and adjust metropolitan science and technology to the service of African social and economic progress.

But doesn't this reasoning repeat one of our great errors? The more Western science progresses, the more it relies upon enormous financial grants, expensive laboratories, mechanical and electronic equipment, and computers. Huge research funds are indispensable. But Africa has no capacity whatever for financing scientific research and related technology. Its few universities are scattered about. The modest scientific research done is financed by Western institutions or grants.

Now the European scientist working in Africa is compensated according to European standards and given "hardship bonuses." But the African scientist must be content with his country's low salary scales, must work in a kind of scientific vacuum, without facilities, without adequate laboratories, with little equipment and fewer grants, and with little public understanding of what he is doing.

Year after year, a majority of African students abroad, do not return home because the absorptive capacity of their nations' economies is so limited that they have little hope of practicing their profession—doctors, engineers, agronomists, chemists, architects, even artists stay abroad. And when they do come back to Africa, a mutation occurs. They go into politics, into the administration, the foreign service, international or inter-African organizations. Very few exercise *their profession*.

There is no doubt, then, that the preparation and formation of scientific and technological study centers in Africa are absolutely necessary.

—How are they to be conceived?

—How can they best be integrated into the realities of modern Africa?

—What can be done to assist them?

I think one step in the right direction would be a well-coordinated crash project to create a wide range of middle-level technicians—midwives, primary-school teachers, nurses, mechanics, accountants, electricians, laboratory staff, agricultural extension workers. This would release the African economies from the heavy burden of financing thousands of European expatriates presently occupying these positions. And, it would create a sound base for later industrialization, scientific research, and related technologies.

Without severing its intimate ties with Europe and the West, the African scientific establishment should look for other models and sources of inspiration and guidance. There are medium-sized countries that have themselves recently emerged from underdevelopment and succeeded in establishing modest but effective scientific and technological structures of their own.

. . . . Here I feel alone. . . . No Western, European interests would agree with me, nor would the African elites, who in their conservatism cling to the established emotional and educational patterns, afraid to replace the familiar with the unknown. . . .

THREE

The
African
Intellectual

T HE MORNING SKY WAS DARK GRAY, HEAVY AND low with rain. The crowns of the palm trees were lost in whitish vapors, and the bougainvillaeas and shrubs were bent from last night's downpour. Muddy, reddish puddles of rainwater studded the driveway. The ground, the air, the sky were steaming with humidity. The Ambassador looked at his watch. Nine A.M. and his car was not yet in sight.

"My driver is late—as usual." He addressed Dr. David, a short, stocky man with black-rimmed eyeglasses, a mop of dark hair over his high forehead. Dr. David was in his third year as scientific adviser on this remote agricultural station. The Ambassador liked him, and took the trouble to visit here at least twice a year. He respected the man's dedication and professional drive; it bordered on missionary zeal.

Dr. David's difficulties were stupendous. He lived here with his wife and two small children in the midst of a huge semi-arid region of some 25,000 square miles; they were 75 miles from the nearest physician or store. No schools, so his wife had begun a makeshift first-grade for their 7-year-old daughter and her African friends. Their 5-year-old son had contracted bilharzia, a serious intestinal disease, from the polluted water of the nearby river. But Dr. David found his work fascinating. After much investigation and experimentation, he had reached certain conclusions which he believed to be extremely important for the future of this barren land. In his opinion, sugar cane could save it from economic oblivion. Cane, irrigated by gravitation with water from the river and grown in sufficient quantities to warrant the construction of a refinery near the center of the region—this was his plan. The African state could thus, in a few years' time, cease its sugar imports, which now cost some $4 million yearly in scarce foreign currency.

Somehow, though, no one in the administration seemed interested. Certainly, nobody of consequence in the ministries concerned offered help or even went out of his way to look at Dr. David's experimental fields or to check the results of his primitive hand-operated sugar press. Even his salary often arrived late.

The Ambassador, however, was convinced that Dr. David's sugar cane scheme was a sound project. Not only would it save millions in foreign currency, it would guarantee employment for at least five hundred families. The Ambassador let it be known —tentatively—that his own government was ready to help finance the project. But even then he could not pierce the wall of obviously simulated official indifference.

Eventually, the President himself told him, in a burst of nervous frankness, that the matter was intimately tied to his country's economic and political relations with France. *"Monsieur l'Ambassadeur,"* the President said, "you know that France is supporting my country with grants amounting to almost $40 million a year. At this very moment, my Foreign Minister is negotiating a most important loan in Paris. And, Excellency, you are well aware that France's antiquated agriculture is in deep trouble in the European Common Market, and that French beet sugar is not only overproduced but overpriced on the world market. But what can I do? Any move from my side, at this point"—the Head of

State nervously repeated the phrase, thumping his fist on the mahogany desk, "at this point would strain our relations with the French Government and could certainly torpedo the economic negotiations now in progress in Paris. Important decisions of this kind are never based on economic and technical considerations alone. In this case and at this moment we can do nothing. We have to wait for a more propitious occasion."

The Ambassador assured him it had never been his intention to complicate relations with France; but he left the presidential palace fuming. "Why wasn't I told before?"

Now he was here at the station, 400 miles from the capital. Sitting on the terrace, he had talked to Dr. David through most of the tropical night. Without involving the President, he wanted David to understand that staying here was now senseless and politically even harmful. But Dr. David did not understand at all. He refused to let himself be drawn into the unknown fields of international economics and politics. To him, everything was clear, proven, rational. Long after midnight, a thunderstorm forced both into the dark, hot living room. The windows had to be closed and shuttered, and the Ambassador could feel his wet shirt glued to his back and the perspiration running down his face, stinging his eyes. He had that terrifying feeling of lacking air, of being about to faint. The rains came suddenly—sheets of water hitting the shutters and the tin roof like heavy stones. He went to bed—and to his astonishment slept through the deluge.

Now, waiting for his car, he watched David's haggard, drawn face. What a sleepless, agonizing night the man must have had. Nothing is more painful than the annihilation of one's dream. He had been wounded, not in his professional standing or personal ambitions but, worse, in his humanity, in his devotion to his neighbor—the black man.

The African director of the station came to join them on the terrace. He and Dr. David urged the Ambassador to postpone his departure till the following day. The rains had damaged the highway, some crossroads were flooded, roadbanks were washed away, and driving would be dangerous. Instantly the Ambassador refused: he wanted to be home by nightfall. One—no, two days were enough for this venture—rain or shine. He would leave.

Then he recalled that he had half promised, in a casual way, to visit one of his African acquaintances from the Foreign Ministry, living not far from here at his mother's home. But no—the rain, the bad road would provide more than an ample excuse for not going. The Ambassador felt impatient.

His car arrived. Abdou, the driver, took his suitcase and opened the door. Handshakes, a few encouraging last words of thanks to Dr. David and his wife, and they were off.

Abdou drove slowly in second gear along the deserted highway. The windshield wipers worked incessantly, cleaning away the muddy water splashing up from the road. Part of the roadbank *had* caved in during the night, and the road was covered with that same reddish water that stretched far across the fields on both sides of the highway. The car labored slowly through the minia-ture lakes, water spouting from the wheels and drumming con-stantly against the sides and bottom of the car. Suddenly, the sun pierced the clouds, brilliantly reflected on the high palm and baobab trees. The desolate expanses of water all around began to shimmer and glitter in the sudden sunlight. No sign of life, however, only the heavy sound of the laboring motor and the mo-notonous dripping of water.

Suddenly, with enormous speed, the car lurched forward. All noise stopped, and then it tilted slowly to the right, deeper and deeper into the soupy water of a flooded ditch. A heavy, frozen silence engulfed everything.

The Ambassador never remembered exactly what happened after that. He must have pushed the left back door open and jumped out. He found himself waist-deep in water. He sensed a burning pain above his right eye, touched his forehead, and looked at his hand: blood. He had cut himself against the car win-dow. He looked about and called for Abdou.

The following chaotic minutes were spent in getting Abdou, who was seemingly in shock, and himself onto higher ground. The Ambassador ceremoniously absolved Abdou from any responsibility for the accident. He asked him where aid and a salvage vehicle could be gotten, eventually persuading Abdou to walk to the next village, some four miles away, and telephone for help—if need be to the governor of the region, whom he knew by sight from official visits and some social events in the capital. Abdou left reluctantly, wading through the muddy waters, looking back, nervous for his abandoned, wounded master. The Ambassador sat down by the deserted road, pressing his handkerchief against his throbbing forehead, disgusted with himself, dazed, and dead tired.

Some time later he was awakened by voices. A skinny old man with a whitish beard, clad in baggy short trousers and a torn shirt, waded toward him and addressed him in the dialect of the region. The Ambassador answered in French. The old man tried again, laughed goodheartedly, winked, turned around and called loudly. Two young boys appeared from behind the immersed car. One of them apparently understood some French, and the Ambassador told the story of his accident. The old man listened to the shouted translation with great calm and dignity, promised help, and waded away, accompanied by the two chattering youngsters.

Everything fell back into motionless calm. All was unruffled stillness. Hours must have passed. No sign of Abdou. No sign of the old man. The Ambassador was thirsty and hungry, and more and more desperate. Then he must have dozed off again, sitting on his suitcase.

Voices again—the old man was back! A leather gourd was slung over his shoulder and in one hand he held flat bread cakes wrapped in a dirty white cloth. He salaamed the Ambassador and presented the gifts. The sour milk from the gourd was delicious and cool, the bread crusty and still warm. The Ambassador at once felt better and began to see the humorous aspect of his helplessness—he was now on the receiving end of all the help and technical assistance he could get from rural Africa! They squatted down together. The Ambassador took out a five-hundred-franc note and presented it with a flourish and thanks—but this gesture seemed to be extremely offensive to the wrinkled old African. He jumped up, shaking his head and talking excitedly, turned about and waded angrily away.

The Ambassador was on his feet. What had gone wrong? "How did I offend this good-hearted old man? Was it not enough money?" No, he must have sinned against some ritual of hospitality, one of the sacred tenets of tribal life. Some elaborate ceremonial must have been slighted. Money was not the countervalue of hospitality for that old African. "What was it then? Where have I transgressed?" The bank note was still in his hand when he heard the heavy purr of an approaching car.

The Ambassador distinguished three people in an open Land Rover—the driver, in police uniform, a tall young man in a long white boubou, a dark red fez on his head, and, next to the driver, Abdou gesturing frantically at him. The vehicle stopped, Abdou jumped down, his white teeth flashing, speechless with joy at seeing his master unharmed. The third man approached, holding his immaculate white robes above the water, and the Ambassador realized that he knew him. This was Alioune Fall, Assistant to the Foreign Minister, the friend he had so casually decided not to visit only a few hours ago.

They had met years ago at U.N. conferences and General Assemblies. Alioune was one of the three top people in the Foreign Office, an intelligent young diplomat who had studied law and political science in Paris, read extensively, spoke English quite well, and was fond of classical music. In New York, he and the Ambassador had frequently gone to Alexander Schneider's quartet concerts at the New School and had enjoyed evenings together at Carnegie Hall. They talked politics reluctantly, avoiding the issues where their tastes and personal viewpoints would differ or clash. In the African capital, their families had met at many embassy parties, and the Ambassador and his wife had visited Alioune's home on the day his first-born was baptized—almost a year ago.

Marie, Alioune's vivacious and intelligent young wife, had met Alioune at the Sorbonne, and they had been married in France. Marie came from a Christian urban family who had lived for three generations in the capital. French was her mother tongue; she was quick-witted and always ready with a smile, a joke. In the eyes of the Ambassador, Marie was the ideal emancipated African woman of the future—intelligent, feminine, professional, and happy with her husband and child. The family was a perfect demonstration that Africa and Europe could amalgamate successfully in a happy home.

Here Alioune was shaking his hand, inquiring about his health, cleaning and bandaging the wound over his eye, helping him into the car. Suddenly, Alioune's expression changed, his smile disappeared, his eyes became distant and earnest, his mouth contracted, his body became rigid. He turned to the old man, who had reappeared from the bush and was standing dejectedly and silently in the middle of the road, holding both hands over his eyes. Alioune uttered a few sharp sentences. The other responded haltingly, lifting his eyes from the ground. Then Alioune walked toward the man, shook his hand, and spoke to him in a soothing, patient tone. On and on went the conversation; then Alioune quickly turned to the Ambassador and asked him, smilingly, for the five-hundred-franc note. Alioune returned to the old man, banknote in hand, and the conversation continued. The old man took the money, greeted the Ambassador with left hand on forehead, and thanked him with much dignity.

Alioune had joined the Ambassador in the car, which started up loudly and moved through a wide puddle covering the road.

Fighting the noise of the shifting gears and the dripping water, Alioune shouted, "That was Ibrahima Sow—the chief of an important clan of my people. They graze their cattle nearby. He likes you, but I had to smooth over a misunderstanding. He thought you wanted to offend him by paying for his milk and bread, so I explained that you wanted only to express your gratitude symbolically.

"You know, hospitality to a stranger is imperative here in our tribal, half-nomadic society. Clans and kinships are closed social groups. A stranger could easily be a messenger of the gods or the spirits sent to test one's faith. As long as you enjoyed his milk and bread, you behaved as expected, but the moment you paid him you frightened the old man. He interpreted your gesture as finding fault with him and his people for their greed."

Alioune laughed. "How do you feel, being the envoy of higher powers?"

"I assure you," the Ambassador smiled, "I was the most uninformed and graceless envoy these powers ever employed. But if I am ever commanded by heaven or earth to report on Ibrahima Sow and his men, I will not spare my praise. They found great favor in mine eyes."

Alioune smiled, kept silent for some moments, then continued in a serious vein. "Leaving aside the biblical analogies, I came at the right moment. Otherwise you would have been their guest tonight—they would have killed one of their best beasts in your honor. They would have fattened you like a goose, and then, my friend, in the dark of your hut an especially beautiful girl would have tried to win your favor. After all, not every girl has the chance to become intimate with a supernatural envoy and perhaps conceive a half-god who would bring fame and wealth to his mother and his people. Your consent to espouse this girl for one night, this—my friend—would be the customary recompense for the traditional tribal hospitality. And not your five hundred francs."

For some time the Ambassador was quiet and thoughtful. He sensed that Alioune was apprehensive of his reaction and expected some half-cynical remark, some flippant white man's joke. He turned to Alioune. "I am sorry I disappointed Chief Sow, but he certainly did not disappoint me. I owe him a debt for having treated me as a special guest and in addition for having given me a lesson in humility."

The car had reached higher ground. The Ambassador smelled the peculiar pungent scent of an African village, of burned charcoal and decomposition. They entered a small town of low mud-brick houses and a few whitewashed cement-block buildings, roofed with rice-straw. The unpaved streets were laid out at right angles. "My home town, Lambéné," said Alioune.

The car stopped in front of a large whitewashed house in the middle of the village. Someone appeared to roll a mat over the mud to the car. Alioune and the Ambassador took off their muddied shoes and slipped into white babouches, and the Ambassador followed his host through the door. In a corner of the spacious, clean room, a few round leather pillows lay on the floor, and some colored reed mats were rolled against the wall. On the windowsill, tiny white teacups and a gleaming copper kettle were placed on a heavy bronze tray. Through the only window and the nearby low door, children's voices, cackling of hens, and the occasional bark of a dog could be heard from the courtyard.

Alioune turned hesitantly to the Ambassador. "If you feel up to it, we should greet my mother first."

Out they went through the other door. They found their muddy shoes on the doorstep, slipped them on, and entered the yard. A crowd of serious barefoot children quickly surrounded them, everyone stretching out his hand to the stranger. They were a well-fed, big-eyed, healthy lot, very impressed with the white man in their yard. Some of the older boys and girls had notebooks and pencils in their hands. Alioune made the presentations.

"This is Daoud. Here, little Awa, come and shake the Ambassador's hand. Oumi, don't be bashful. Hamidou, go first and wipe your nose and then greet our friend. Here is Moussa, the brightest pupil and the pride of the family, and here Mamadou, who has decided to become an officer."

The children stepped aside and followed them silently from a respectful distance.

They crossed the yard toward a large open cooking shed. Here, by the hearth, stood Alioune's mother—a tall, straight, heavy woman, clad in a dark blue boubou that covered even her feet. Around her head she wore a low turban of the same material, and a beautiful heavy golden necklace gleamed against the dark skin of her neck. The Ambassador was fascinated by her strong face —long and heartshaped, and without a wrinkle. Her large, almond eyes, very luminous, looked intensely into the eyes of her guest. She turned her head to Alioune, smiled lightly, with a mixture of pity and compassion, and walked, hand outstretched, to welcome his guest. Taking the Ambassador's hand, she led him into the shed and seated him on a low stool brought by a shy, attractive young girl clad in a long African dress, her sleeping baby securely tied around her slim waist. The young woman kept her eyes on the ground and retreated hurriedly, but the old woman called her back, and the girl returned to her side, motionless and tense, eyes fixed to the ground. Alioune's mother addressed a sharp sentence to her son. Alioune, embarrassed, looked nervously at the Ambassador and said stiffly, "Please meet my new wife, Aminata."

The Ambassador was dumbfounded, but his professional training stood him in good stead. The instant of uneasiness was caught quickly. He shook hands with Aminata, addressing her in French. The young woman looked around helplessly, first to her mother-in-law, then to Alioune, who translated in short sentences. The girl answered inaudibly, then looked up, straight and wide-eyed, into the Ambassador's face.

"Too young—insecure and out of place, poor girl. Poor Alioune, for that matter," reflected the Ambassador.

At that moment, a strident, high-keyed voice began to be heard, chanting continuously, rhythmically. Everyone was silent for a moment.

"That is our muezzin calling for the evening prayer," said Alioune.

The Ambassador was suddenly exhausted, his headache was returning, and he needed to rest. They took leave of the old woman and returned to the house. The Ambassador undressed in his little square room and lay on the low bed, the *tara*. The muezzin's voice had ceased. Through the open window, the Ambassador saw Alioune in the middle of the yard, kneeling on a mat, praying, his head from time to time touching the ground. Children were playing, and the Ambassador heard the cackling of hens and a dog's bark.

He woke with a start. The darkness was heavy. He remembered his accident, the arrival at Alioune's house. He felt much better now, but thirsty and hungry. He dressed, and Alioune appeared to invite him to supper. In the courtyard, the night was cool and clear, the sky studded with stars. Embers glowed red in the hearth. The Ambassador washed his hands and face in water from an earthen jar, and followed Alioune to the open shed, where a low table and two stools had been placed before the charcoal fire. Alioune turned down his kerosene lamp and busied himself with kettles over the fire. He returned with a teakettle and two deep earthen bowls. The tea was strong and sweet, and in the bowls were mounds of steamed spicy rice, chopped vegetables, and shredded chicken in a lemon sauce, the famous *yassa* dish of the region.

They ate for some time in silence. Then the Ambassador took courage.

"Alioune, this has been an astonishing day. I experienced emotions and events which I do not wholly understand. I don't want to pry into your life for curiosity's sake but I would like to understand you, to follow you. Who is your mother? What do you represent here, and where is Marie?"

Alioune moved slightly, and his set face shone like copper in the purple light from the hearth. He did not answer, then slowly and quickly he spoke, choosing his words.

"I really do not believe that 'knowing is understanding.' I have learned that we both, white and black, are prisoners of our own conditional moralities. We are ready to accept the unbelievable if it is couched in the impersonal language of natural sciences. But try to break away from tradition, from customs established in the forgotten past, and you will find yourself chastised and punished like an outcast. Yes, I am ready to talk about myself, not because you, my foreign friend, can help me, but because I feel that an unknown destiny, a mysterious chain of events, has brought us together. We Africans respond to the mysterious. We leave nothing to chance. Our senses are tuned to the improbable. So I am attracted by it, and at the same time its possible consequences frighten me. There is a tremendous attraction in the certainty of immovability and the permanence of nature."

Alioune lit a cigarette and poured hot tea into their cups.

"Remember Chief Ibrahima Sow? Look at my mother—there you find the key to your questions and my problems. My grandfather served the colonial administration and became one of the first African regional prefects. But his *real* standing and power were inherited. He belonged to a long line of rulers who guided and led our people for generations. My great-grandfather, Amar Alioune, fought the French, and his final stand at Aayar is part of our national history."

The Ambassador remembered that last epic struggle, with Amar Alioune and a few survivors surrounded by a large French military unit, intending to die fighting in the morning. At sunrise the French company was arranged in parade order, trumpets sounding and flags flying, and Amar Alioune was received by the French captain with full honors. That morning concluded the French conquest of the country.

"My mother," continued Alioune, "was born into an old aristocratic family on the northern border of our country. She knew about my father's family from the ballads and the tales of the griots, and illiterate woman though she was, she took over my absent father's prerogatives as the ruler of his people after their marriage. You see, my father lived in France for many years, received a good French military education, and became one of our first officers in the French Army; he lived abroad most of the time, following his regiment from Morocco to Indochina.

"You know, there are no tribal sovereigns left in Africa. An ordinary policeman has more administrative power than any chief. But my mother ruled through and by the people's wish. In their mind she belongs to the line of ancestors who created our community from the voids of the desert, who fought the Arab slave traders, the marauding Moors, and the invading French. Yes, we are devout Muslims, but we are *black* Muslims, not Arabs. My mother's words and acts are sanctified by tradition, and her life is consecrated to the defense of this glorified past against the strange and suffocating future.

"My father died in Indochina. Like so many others of his generation, he wanted to leave Africa behind. They studied hard, and they learned to be black Europeans—'white Negroes,' as we say. But very seldom were they able to return and take their place among their own people. My father tried hard to find a synthesis between the white man's world and his African background. He was one of our first true African nationalists, but he himself was incapable of reintegrating into his old social system of caste and kinship. He tried once or twice, but found it impossible. Later, he married a French woman who loved him, who shared his military life, and who gave him a home and children. He was a dashing man, very good-looking and intelligent. Yes, in Paris I have another home—two sisters and a brother as French as French can be. But I doubt very much that my father ever found peace. A courageous soldier, five times wounded, decorated with all the medals prowess can bestow. But he never felt easy. He always felt guilty of having deserted his people in their hour of need. He was a lonely man.

"Toward the end, his dream was to lead a modern African army of our independent African state. But he felt misunderstood, repulsed, and repudiated by his own people. So he reacted antagonistically, even hostilely, to his rural tribal background. Only in the de-Africanized cities did he find friends and an attentive audience. Between our political and intellectual leaders and the people on the land, there exists a complete lack of confidence— much open opposition and even defiance. Luckily no one is ready for a showdown. The rural population has no ideology and no political force to do away with the Europeanized government in the city; and the government is too weak to fight the traditional seats of power, the tribal beliefs and hallowed customs. It is a dangerous sort of armistice, a kind of stagnant balance.

"You must remember that the Europe known in rural Africa for the last 300 years is still the Europe of slave-traders and imperial colonists. Certainly not a Europe one can trust or cooperate with. Never forget: the slave trade depleted Africa by one third and dislocated most of its population. The shattered survivors have found a refuge in their old beliefs and traditions, the emotional security needed for survival. In the history of Africa, especially in the subconscious of our people, the white man has proven beyond a doubt his ability to destroy our social fabric. Here is my mother's and my people's dilemma. My personal problems are but an outgrowth of the general problem. You must understand, there is no privacy in African life. You are part and parcel of a whole. You are a member of a body—one leaf on a tree. The leaf grows dry and disappears, but the tree is permanent, immortal, and therefore holy."

Alioune fell silent. He put some charcoal on the embers. The Ambassador lit a cigarette. "I follow you well, but please," he asked haltingly, "how precisely has this affected your private life? We all carry on our shoulders the weight of our past and the shadows of our inconsistencies. You have made me understand your father and your mother. I understand their attitude and their motivations, but I do not yet grasp your own disposition, your individual attitude toward your social surroundings."

Alioune leaned his head on his hand and said in a sharp voice, "I am sorry, but the difficulty is yours, my friend. You have to furnish the mental and emotional understanding. I have been talking about my mother and father because I inherited their attitudes, their doubts, their duplicity, their tragedy. My father, a white African in the service of the colonial master, cut himself off from his people. His assimilation into French culture and society did not fool anyone, least of all himself. He was always a stranger at the gates. I remember him once near tears when he told me about the vulgarities, the suave racial allusions his daughters had to suffer at school in Paris because of their father's color. No, complete assimilation is finally impossible. I think he realized this late in life, especially when he found out that his eldest daughter, the darker one, hated everything French and white and associated only with African students. She begged him to return to Africa. The deep irony of the situation was that her Africa was ridiculously utopian—a permanent blue sky, laughing black women, and intelligent, cultivated black men. Then my father knew that he had deprived his children of their African birthright.

"After his death, my mother waited two years before asking me to come back home 'to take my father's place.' I hesitated for over a year. My life in Paris was intellectually rewarding. I was successful in my studies. I had near and dear European and African friends, and I was deeply in love with Marie. I had lived in Paris for five years—studying for classes, going out with girls, discussing world politics with my radical student friends, demonstrating in the streets, distributing revolutionary tracts. Imagine, I forgot for days on end the color of my skin!"

Alioune turned toward the hearth and continued slowly.

"My mother's letter was like a time bomb. At first I simply refused to consider the possibility of going back. Then little by little I began to feel like an actor on a foreign stage performing my own life's comedy. Once I had finished studying, Paris became a dead-end street. The image of my father, and his family, reminded me constantly that I had no alternative. Like many of my fellow African students, I was fascinated by and proud of Africa's newly-won independence, involved in African and international politics. But like my progressive friends, I had acquired a cold and remote anthropological attitude toward Africa. I had even given up the practice of Islam. I had scientific solutions for all our ills. The correct application of social and economic science would solve Africa's backwardness; the needed social revolution would occur through the progressive radicalization and politicization of our peasantry. Naïve scientific answers and easy dialectical solutions.

"It was then that Marie and I decided to marry. I wanted to return to Africa and present my mother and all others who cared with a *fait accompli:* to have married outside my caste and tribe. I wanted to tell them once and for all that my personal opinions and political convictions were my own concern and my personal responsibility.

"We returned home, but there was no home for either of us. My mother refused to receive Marie. She had already chosen Aminata as my first wife, the fourteen-year-old daughter of a paramount chief up-river. I visited my mother once and returned to

live in the capital, where I started in the Foreign Ministry. My
salary was large enough to permit us to live simply and decently.
Marie started to work as a social worker in the army.

"Then, unpredictably, almost unconsciously, our lives started
to change. Marie's family had been city-dwellers for three generations. They are as assimilated to Western civilization and ways of
life as Africans can be. They dress like Europeans, they spend
their holidays in France whenever they can afford to. They did
not lightly accept the fact that Marie had married a Muslim, but
they were shocked by my mother's repudiation of their daughter.
You see, this is not a question of right or wrong: an African
mother can never be wrong. As long as she lives, her child owes
her allegiance and obedience. She is the living link in the unending chain that binds the ancestor to the unborn. Hers is the obligation to demand unwavering discipline and unquestionable faith
in our beliefs and traditions. That is her sacred role and duty, in
which she is comforted and helped by gods, ancestors, spirits—and
by society. An African mother's happiness, her life's content and
accomplishment is her child. But she will never condone his leaving the ranks. She will fight a rebellious son with all the might
at her disposal. My mother never openly criticized my father. He
was never her responsibility. But for me, her son, she is responsible. Through her son, her physical existence receives its ultimate
justification; through him she reaches immortality, becoming another link in the chain of hallowed ancestors, heroes, and teachers
which insure the survival of our race.

"Marie's parents are assimilated, but they are Africans, and my
mother's attitude weighed heavily on them. Was it superstition,
the feeling of some future evil endangering our marriage? I don't
know. They went for help and counsel from one marabout to another. They returned more upset than ever. Marie was pressured
into lighting candles, praying, and carrying amulets. Don't mis-
understand this. In Africa, cult is culture. Where and when did
the irrational and unreal mingle with the realities of our lives? I
don't know. But soon our lives were clouded and heavy with foreboding and anxiety."

Alioune poured more tea into the cups. He lit another cigarette and continued pensively.

"There was another factor. It all started some weeks after our arrival in the capital. One afternoon, when I got home from the Ministry, I found a delegation of elders, chiefs, priests, and griots waiting in my courtyard—among them some cousins and uncles of mine. They had traveled two days to see me, and they were asking me to come home, to take my place as the heir of Amar Alioune. They did not offer titles of honor, nor did they make promises. They only wanted me to return, to lead and guide them, and to insure the continuity of their world.

"At first I was upset, even hostile, but their dignified simplicity touched me deeply. I felt again, as I had felt in Paris, the strangeness and pretentiousness of my life. And for the first time I felt that my people needed me.

"They remained in my house for two days and nights. By the time they had left, I knew I could never make a final break with my past. These people may be primitive—there is much objectionable superstition and cruelty in our customs and beliefs. But, my friend, they exist side by side with much beauty, with great treasures of human wisdom, and with an endearing nobility of character.

"After that, not a week went by without relatives, elders, old friends, and simply people of ours requesting my hospitality. Often they came only to ask advice on matters concerning their farms, their herds, their families. Others needed help in finding a job or wanted my opinion or intervention in their dealings with the government. Without having aspired to it, I found myself to be their official spokesman and mentor in the capital, the person they trusted. You might ask whether I misused my position in helping these peasants and shepherds to obtain their lawful rights and to see justice done. Many of us in the administration carry a similar burden. We all try to help. It is a simple fact of life, beyond the limits of right or wrong. How can a man from the South believe that someone from the North will do him justice? They have fought and competed for centuries. Nationalism and patriotism are great words, but they are new words in our vocabulary, and only words.

"Months later I was summoned for my first audience with the Head of State. You are well aware of his European culture, his wide intellectual interests. But he also possesses great African assets—an uncanny intuition and insight into the affairs of our different regions, and a deep understanding of the collective psychology of our different tribes and peoples. To the outsider, these traits are not well-known, but they made him our Head of State.

"He congratulated me on a forthcoming promotion and asked me about the problems of my people—their attitudes, political opinions, and their national reliability. He had detailed and exact information about some religious fanatics who had tried to induce them not to pay taxes to 'the unbelievers in the city.' And there was growing tension between two important kinships in the North. More particularly, the smuggling of cattle and merchandise across the border posed a grave problem. The President gave me to understand that he needed me to pacify our region. He knew that police or army intervention would only aggravate the situation and engender distrust and hatred against him, his government, and everything the 'capital' stands for. He needed an unofficial mediator, capable of translating his policy into the language of my people. The mediator in today's Africa is a very necessary and important person. He is the conciliator between regional interests and our national policies. He carries a tremendous responsibility. Indeed, the most important mediators are in the President's cabinet, but others receive major or minor positions in the administration.

"My own future is unlikely to be in the administration, but in national politics on the executive level. An elderly cousin of my father's is now Minister of Information and Telecommunications. He has represented our region in the President's cabinet since independence. I have the feeling that the President is ready to replace him with someone younger, with more drive and initiative. But my cousin is still powerful in our region. The older generation of chiefs and elders do not shift easily their allegiance to someone of my age. Also, some of the most influential and powerful chiefs are tied by very strong economic incentives to his political fortune. But it isn't easy for my cousin either. He is getting old. The strains of living and working on two commitments separated by a distance of 500 miles are too much for him, and he spends more and more of his time in the capital, where his life is very comfortable indeed. Because of this, the younger men feel neglected and want him replaced. They want someone younger in the executive—someone capable of bringing into our region work and money, schools, a doctor and clinics. Many of my people expect me to challenge and succeed him. However, my capacity as a provider is not yet an established fact. I will have to work hard to prove myself and to establish my political image."

Alioune looked questioningly at his friend. "You have helped me greatly with the sugar cane scheme. Everyone thinks I brought you out here for that reason, and many feel that its momentary failure is due to my cousin's jealousy and his destructive response to my challenge. I hope you don't mind?"

The Ambassador felt suddenly uncomfortable. He had never taken regional politics into account in dealing with this project. Nothing is ever simple in Africa, he reflected, and concentrated again on his friend's words.

"I don't want or need to defend our political system. It is certainly not an Anglo-Saxon-style democracy. The balance of political power in Africa does not rest with political parties, but with regional, linguistic, tribal, and religious components. Anywhere in Africa where the regional balance has been upset, there you witness the tragedies of civil war, so-called revolutions, secessions. Think of the Congo, and now Biafra. So if and when Africa starts to modernize its social and economic structures, it will be first and foremost the feat of us unknown mediators—reconciling the far-away, destitute regions with a progressive national administration."

Alioune seemed to expect the Ambassador's approval. Then he continued talking in a low, impersonal tone.

"I think my conversation with the President brought my per-

sonal crisis to its conclusion. I had to take my place. I needed to
return for my own peace of mind, because there was no other
place where I fitted into the natural order of African life. Here
I was truly needed by my people and by my government. So, I
confronted my African destiny. We have a saying, 'useless as a
monkey's skin—good neither for a shoemaker nor for a prayer
mat.' I didn't want to become a monkey's skin.

"At the beginning, Marie understood my problems, my struggles. But, with the passing of time, she could not follow me. I
don't think my second marriage to Aminata came as a total shock
to her. Marie is a Christian and an urbanite, but she is an African,
and we are used to polygamy since the dawn of time. The real,
the deadly blow came from my mother, who didn't allow her to
share my life here."

Alioune's voice trembled slightly. "Two weeks ago, our divorce
became final, official. I . . ." His voice broke. He sat motionless
in the dark. Only his rapid breathing betrayed his pain. The
embers had died out. Overhead, the clear dark sky glittered with
countless stars. On the eastern horizon a spreading paleness announced the coming of the morning.

The two men did not move for a long time. Suddenly, nearby,
a cock sounded his triumphant loud crow. Both were startled and
shifted in their seats, waking up awkwardly to their surroundings,
putting themselves together.

Alioune broke the heavy silence, his voice devoid of emotion.
"I apologize for the late hour, for having kept you so long. Let's
go to bed for a few hours. In the morning, after the Fadjar prayer,
my car will take us to the capital."

Both men walked wordlessly back to the house. At the door, the
Ambassador thanked his friend, haltingly, unsure of himself. He
did not want to use words that sounded inadequate or hollow.

A knock at the door. The Ambassador sat up in bed with a
start. Eyes closed, uncertain of his surroundings, he answered the
insistent knocking, instinctively in his native language. The

knocking stopped, and he heard the pearly laughter and running bare feet of a girl. He dressed, opened the door, and found on the ground a large bowl and two jars of water. He washed and shaved, feeling surprisingly fit and well. Alioune arrived and invited him for breakfast. Today, Alioune was dressed *à la Européene* in a dark blue suit of light tropical material, fitting tightly and accentuating his lanky body. His shirt was gleaming white, his tie light blue. He laughed loudly as he shook hands with the Ambassador, guiding him to the main room of the house. A barefoot servant brought a steaming coffee pot to their table. There was French marmalade and exquisite warm bread.

After breakfast, Alioune asked the Ambassador to accompany him as he took leave of his mother. They found her in another room, standing before an open window. Her low tara-bed was covered with an attractive, colorful carpet. On a high, round table, covered with a heavy purplish spread, stood dozens of photographs, some slightly tinted, others pale and faded: group pictures of solemn people dressed in their best white boubous, looking straight and tense into the camera, pictures of matrons surrounded by big-eyed children, and several photos of a straight tall man, smiling in a French Army uniform. A large gold-framed mirror gleamed from one of the walls. In the corner stood a heavy big trunk, black with age. There were a few white animal-fur rugs, French straight-backed chairs, and in the corner a beautiful escritoire.

The old woman was dressed in a traditional robe—immaculate, white, flowing—a white scarf on her head. When she saw her son she stepped forward, and the Ambassador noted the easy grace of her movements. Through Alioune she asked her guest the conventional questions: How had he slept? Had he enjoyed his breakfast? With a twinkle in her eyes, she told him that he should return soon and be her guest before another natural disaster forced him to accept her hospitality. She shook a limp hand with her guest and turned to face her son.

The Ambassador was impressed. "Madame has dismissed me," he thought, half seriously. Alioune kissed his mother on both cheeks. She had put the palms of her hands over his eyes, murmuring a prayer.

Stepping outside, they found the official black Citroen surrounded by children. Near the wall, a group of elderly men waited in respectful distance and silence. Alioune greeted everyone, talked briefly, and returned to the car. The two servants brought the suitcases. Then Aminata appeared, her baby wrapped at her back, his tiny feet showing above her waist. Her long colorful dress emphasized her adolescent figure. Aminata gave Alioune a parcel wrapped in white cloth. He kissed his wife lightly, stroked and kissed the forehead of his son, and waved goodbye. The car moved slowly toward the highway.

They both remained silent, each looking out at the sunbathed landscape. After the rain, the fields were covered with deep green vegetation. The palms and baobab trees looked newly washed. Little herds of cattle and sheep grazed here and there. A feeling of pastoral calm, of springtime permeated the air. The rainy season had started. . . .

"Confessions cannot be undone," reflected the Ambassador. "They demand absolution or punishment—at any rate, a response. But last night I kept quiet, and he sensed my incapacity to relate, to verbalize my sympathy for his problems."

Alioune felt tired, insecure, and angry with himself. "Why have I talked so much, opened myself to this comparative stranger? What devil possessed me?" He had committed an unpardonable indiscretion by talking about himself. Had not Palmerston said, "A diplomat knows no friends or enemies, only the interests of his mission"? Why had he burdened his sympathetic European friend with the woes and worries of his life? He felt suddenly very much alone. He closed his eyes.

"Alioune," said the Ambassador, "I do appreciate your confidence in me. The evening at your home was an unforgettable experience. I don't know how to express my feelings for you, for Marie, your mother, your wife, but I want you to know that I do understand you, possibly better than you think. . . . With all the differences of your African background, the differentness of your customs and beliefs, you are going through agonies of read-justment and reappraisal which are common to all of us. True, Western society may be more permissive, but still, her punish-ments are harsh and vengeful. Africa is less flexible because she defends herself against the assault of foreign influences. Your so-ciety is still afraid of change and compromise. In the West we have subcultures where an outsider can find refuge and relative peace. In Africa, you choose at your peril. I only hope that the society of your children will be more comprehensive—in other words, that your pains and struggles will not have been in vain."

Alioune followed his friend's halting words with growing in-tensity. When he answered, it was with a desperate note in his voice.

"You may be right in relative historical terms, but what does that mean in our life span—for my generation? After our long sojourns in the fields of Western knowledge and technology, we find ourselves outside our own society. Instead of confronting tribalism, religious superstition, orthodoxy, we accommodate our-selves to them, if only for appearance's sake. We adopt traditional and rhetorical postures, in the facile belief that we can evolu-tionize our native structures from within. Very few of us have been true revolutionaries. Most of those you will find in prison or in the cemeteries. Deep down, I envy and admire them, the un-known Lumumbas and Luthulis of Africa.

"An African head of state has only two clear choices: The first one is the destruction of our antiquated social structures, the use of brute physical violence and political terror, forcing our popula-tion into a new mold. After all, the use of physical violence has many advocates. The colonialists—and especially the Communists —succeeded in forcing modernization and industrialization upon unwilling, reactionary, rural societies. It has been tried in Africa under the most diverse trademarks: Nkrumahism, Chinese Com-munism, Soviet Leninism. Various colonels gave it a rightist twist. But the results are far from satisfactory. The Soviets say that we are not yet ready "objectively" to reap the benefits of a social revo-lution because we have as yet not developed a class struggle, no

elite party of professional revolutionaries, no class-conscious working class. To me, the reasons seem different. But anyway, what
matters is that dictatorships based on the use of physical violence
have simply failed to effect the hoped-for revolution.

"The second choice consists in exercising political power
through the medium of a permanent dialog, an African palaver
between the central power and all the other focuses of social and
economic forces: regions, labor unions, sects, tribes, and professional interests. There is little leeway for compromise. Our economy is weak, our administration inefficient, our population unruly.
It is impossible to satisfy even their most urgent needs and requests.
So the art of statesmanship is learning how to compromise in the
division of a nonexistent cake. It may not be efficient or productive, but it is very humane and very African. Our original contribution to the science of statecraft."

Alioune laughed lightly and continued as if talking to himself.

"My generation is neither here nor there. During the day we
are educated European technocrats. But then comes the evening,
the weekend, the holiday, and we return to our old ways of life
—into a complicated polygamic family, into a caste system, into a
parasitical kinship structure, which obliges me at this moment to
take care of, feed, and house some twelve cousins, uncles, and
other relatives for whom I don't care and whom I don't wish to
know. Most of us reassimilate. We try to forget and not mind any
more. Our peace of mind, our private lives, our political futures
are better served this way. But from there stems our personal im-
mobility and uncertainty, our incapacity to move on.

"Let me illustrate: Our village gas station is owned by one of
our elders. I told him half a dozen times that one day he would
be arrested for mixing boiled water or kerosene in his gasoline.
And just before you arrived, a policeman did come to arrest him.
He came crying to me and it was my duty, my African duty, to
secure his release. A few weeks ago, a group of our men were
arrested for having stolen rice and seeds from trucks going north
to the relief region. Well, they had stolen them, but for the
account of an Arab trader who meanwhile disappeared. They

aren't thieves in the African sense. They would never have taken a grain from their neighbors. Tribal law is ferocious about stealing your neighbors' food but doesn't have much to say about taking it away from 'others.' Of course, I'll have to look after them, and try to have them released as easily as possible.

"Let me tell you a word about one of our most dangerous illnesses, the cancer of independent Africa: corruption. You know our constitutions, our codes, our judicial systems are modeled on the European pattern. Graft, extortion, theft, robbery, manslaughter, and murder are clearly defined criminal offenses and are dealt with as such. As it happens, the legal concepts of tribal law are different, and they often conflict with the official law of the land—which is counteracted and neutralized by that amorphous and tenacious majority of our rural population.

"Take a case of murder. Tribal law is less interested in its moral and social implications than in the material aspects of the case. What will happen to the murdered man's family and kinship group? What was he worth? How many people depended on him? What caste did he stem from? The elders negotiate with the killer's kinship group for as high a blood price as possible. There is no idea of punishing the killer. He will be punished by his own family, who pay for his crime. Only if the long deliberations between the elders fail will there be a blood feud between villages or tribal units—burning houses, killing cattle and people, a small civil war. But no one sees any advantage in pursuing the murderer before a tribunal."

Alioune sat back and lit a cigarette. The car had arrived at a railway crossing. A long line of trucks, delivery vans, and dilapidated little buses overcrowded with passengers waited at the barrier. Alioune's driver did not wait in line. Giving a friendly sign with his hand here, calling a name there, he drove on the left side of the road straight to the barrier. No one objected, no one asked a question. Everyone was cheerful, friendly.

"The new ruling class," mused the Ambassador. "After all, in the capital the traffic stays immobilized for hours while the Head of State passes quickly through, accompanied by ten motor-

cyclists, going a few blocks to the theater, a church, a mosque."
The train passed. The barrier went up. Their car shot diag-
onally into the right lane. Alioune sat in the corner, given over to
his thoughts. Then he continued pensively.

"Our two most vicious social and economic problems are the
bride price and the kinship festivities. They are at the root of
what we call the evil of corruption. Look at my driver. Moussa
is now 30 years old. He served for seven years in the French
Army. He receives an excellent salary—almost $80 a month. But
he cannot marry. His bride will cost him $600 or more. He has
been engaged for the past three years and has already paid more
than half the agreed price. But his father fell ill, and one of his
little brothers came to the city to stay with him. The brother
doesn't have a job, so Moussa has to look after him. Family obligations supersede personal considerations. The girl likes Moussa,
but she is getting older and wants to marry. He simply doesn't
have the money. A few weeks ago, her father wanted to marry
her off to a rich old merchant with three wives and grown children. Moussa was lucky; his fiancée refused—this time. He has a
chance as long as the girl waits for him or can withstand family
pressure.

"If she is married off to someone else, Moussa has very little
chance of getting his money back. There are no receipts or witnesses. Our courts are filled with lawsuits about this subject—
which again cost great amounts of unavailable money. Parliament
decreed a law limiting the bride price to a maximum of $100 for
a virgin and established scales for a divorcée or a widow with
children. But that is all window dressing. The status of the girl's
family, her beauty and attractiveness are still expressed by the
taman, the bride price. No laws can change this custom, because
from the lawmakers down to the last policeman, everyone has a
vested interest in keeping the bride price as high as possible. In
African society, the oldest age group rules over the younger. Why
should the elders give up such an important economic privilege?
The younger generation cannot change the pattern without up-
setting the whole of our social fabric."

"Please tell me, Alioune," interrupted the Ambassador, "what happens to the bride price once it is paid? After all, this is an important sum of money, a yearly wage for a professional worker."

"The answer, my friend, is nothing of any economic consequence. The money is neither invested nor used to give the young couple a decent start in life. It is simply eaten up in celebrations, in the purchase of new clothes for the parents, gold jewelry for the mother, and maybe new clothes for the bride's sisters and brothers. Almost all of it goes to enhance the social status of her parents, which is done by lavish entertainment on an African scale. A sack of rice is bought, a sheep is slaughtered. Every member of the family and the whole neighborhood is invited. The tamtam is sounded; the youngsters dance. An invited griot recites and sings for hours, acclaiming the hospitality, the valor, and the position of the host, his family, and his ancestors. Festivities go on for one or two days. Nothing is too expensive, everything has to appear rich and plentiful. The next day there is literally nothing left. Then the bride is sent back to her prospective husband to ask for more money, even a few francs, because really her family is hungry. Or, very often, the bride's father stops working and lives on the proceeds of the bride price, especially if he has more than one daughter to give away.

"In a tribe's subsistence economy, the collective festivities were a form of dividing among the old, poor, or weak members the spoils of a successful hunt or victorious skirmish. But a poor money economy like ours cannot afford popular extravagances of this kind, an economic waste on this grandiose scale.

"These are the two most important causes of corruption in our society, and they give you the reason why we have such difficulties in fighting our national vice. An official taking a bribe is not usually stealing for himself. He simply takes from the unknown 'others' and gives the proceeds to his or his wife's kinship family. Reasons and needs abound: illness, bride price, festivities, and celebrations, all steeped in custom and tradition. He too is dividing the spoils of a successful hunt. Suddenly, he is able to appear as a provider. His social standing and prestige are enhanced. Almost overnight, he becomes a man of consequence and importance. If he is caught and convicted, in our eyes he is a thief, but to his family—that is, to 80 per cent of the African population—he is a persecuted victim.

"Certainly there are also cases of bribery on a large commercial scale. Business contracts are sometimes signed with whoever offers the highest bribe—these are often well-established Western firms. We deal with offenses of this kind about as well as other governments in the East or West."

By now they were no longer in the arid eastern zone but in the more humid central section of the country. Nearing the capital, they passed more and better dressed people and more cars and trucks. Here and there they could distinguish the red-tiled roof of a European's house hidden among high trees and flaming red bougainvillaea. On the left, the Atlantic Ocean came into sight.

"I'm afraid you may have misunderstood me," said Alioune suddenly. "I am not blindly opposed to traditional Africa. My generation fights neither Africa's religious nor its ancestral customs. Much of our social customs and religious belief is beautiful, more satisfying than anything comparable in European civilization. The extended family provides an infinite source of human acceptance and warmth. The kinship family takes care of its ill, of the old and weak. An African lives from cradle to grave in a kind of warm human companionship which is unknown in the West. There is no alienation. The belonging to his group and family is his unquestionable birthright. He is part and parcel of a mystic, collective personality. The rural African refuses to become a lonely individual responsible for his deeds before a cold, depersonalized, anonymous society.

"Tell me. Is he wrong? Have we offered or given him something better? Why should he believe suddenly in words—without the proof of deeds? Our money economy is growing slowly, but he doesn't yet benefit from it, since industries and economic institutions are in or near the cities. Hospitals, schools, movies—all that is for the urban population. He is forced to pay taxes for services he does not need or understand. He is convinced that the city is exploiting him. And the city is too powerful to be confronted directly, openly. Therefore, he too needs a mediator.

"The mediator, that's me again," said Alioune, smiling broadly. "My generation, we are the real marabouts and witch doctors of our time: men for all seasons, promising the impossible, adapting to the unacceptable, masters of improvisation."

The car had slowed down. Traffic was dense and slow. The driver had to dodge cars, trucks, little carriages drawn by emaciated horses or donkeys. Crowds of Africans walked busily on both sides of the road carrying bundles, or cycling along. Slow-moving women in long flowing robes, children at their waists, baskets on their heads, statuesquely crossed the road. Barefoot teenage boys in rags played football. Groups of chatting, laughing women sat at the edge of the highway behind displays of a few coconuts, mangoes, and guava fruits arranged neatly on a mat. The car was in the suburbs of the capital.

"In a few minutes I'll be home," thought the Ambassador with immense relief.

Again, Alioune turned toward him abruptly and said, "I want you to know that I greatly esteem your unsuccessful efforts to place a sugar plant in my region. I intervened personally twice with our Head of State. This time foreign interests were too powerful for us. But this may change, sooner or later. Every Head of State has to compromise, to weigh one risk against another. The political situation here may force him to change his mind—or his political preferences. If at all possible, I would like you not to cancel the project but to keep it in abeyance. You would do me a great favor."

The Ambassador was surprised and a trifle upset by Alioune's request. Then he suddenly understood the President's frank and apologetic posture at his last audience. Apparently even Alioune's warm hospitality and friendship were also based upon a wrong premise. Both men believed that he, the Ambassador, conceived and supported the sugar project as some kind of calculated long-range investment in Alioune's political future. They both believed it, erroneously, and for different reasons. The Ambassador laughed good-naturedly.

"Alioune, I thank you for the compliments, but they are undeserved. I simply intended to cooperate with your government on a project that I found economically promising and socially beneficial for your country. You can rest assured we have not shelved it definitely. For the time being it is simply being put on that well-known ice."

The car had entered Embassy Row and stopped in front of the Ambassador's residence. His gardener came running out and started to open the heavy gate. The Ambassador shook Alioune's hand warmly.

"Please let us dine together soon, possibly tomorrow evening? We will be alone and could go on with our conversation. There are questions and even some answers that come to mind."

Alioune looked doubtful: he did not know if this was possible, if he was available, but he certainly would phone tomorrow morning.

The Ambassador watched the disappearing car. He had a feeling that Alioune would not accept his invitation. "In Laméné I was his honored house guest, brought to his hated and beloved home by sheer coincidence. . . . He must be very lonely there. My appearance was fortuitous—and useful for his political ambitions. There he felt the need to unburden himself. He needed a father-confessor, someone who understood the language of his anxieties, someone who was ready to listen but not to judge or talk. Now we have returned to the city. Confessions here are signs of weakness. Alioune takes his torn personality, his divided loyalties, very seriously. He does not expect pity or understanding. What a lonely man he is!"

The Ambassador walked through his well-kept garden toward the front stairs. The telephone rang insistently in the living-room. "Home again," he thought.

FOUR

Afrique
and
Africa

H IS CAR STOPPED WITH A SCREECH IN FRONT
of the presidential palace. The door was opened quickly by the
Assistant Chief of Protocol, a tall, graying African in a morning
coat and striped trousers, the heavy chain of his office around his
neck and at least five French military decorations adorning his
chest. "Dressed à la Palais de l'Elysée," mused the Ambassador,
"or like a sommelier in a good Paris restaurant." He passed and
greeted with a nod the two huge, red-trousered, red-fezzed Spahis
—at attention, sabers drawn. The Assistant Chief of Protocol led
him toward the enormous half-circular white marble staircase.
"Twenty-two steps," thought the Ambassador.

The heat and humidity were suffocating, and with each step
perspiration ran down his back. Up they went—ceremoniously,
slowly, to the massive front door of the palace. This door was the
Ambassador's delight: perfectly rectangular, some twenty feet
high, of solid oak, ornamented with massive bronze hinges and
doorknob handles of heroic proportions.

77

Inside, the foyer was quiet and dark, so immense that its corners were lost in the shadows. The Ambassador needed a moment to collect himself, to adjust his eyes to the sudden change. At his right, two officers at an Empire desk jumped to attention. Behind them, the official, larger-than-life, gold-framed photograph of the Head of State looked down upon the immense room. He was posed in front of an interminable bookshelf, dressed in formal clothes, the heavy gold chain of office falling from his neck and shoulders, his left hand resting on two bound volumes on a low table. He looked intelligent, stern, uncompromising, and uncomfortable. "No wonder," thought the Ambassador and hastened toward his guide, waiting for him at the bottom of the red-carpeted staircase. Up they went again. "Thirty-two," counted the Ambassador, panting and perspiring. He was shown into a small waiting room.

The deep ottomans, finished in heavy red plush, faced each other. High-backed plush armchairs surrounded a low table covered with official publications. From the opposite wall, a picture of the President looked at him again, this time inquiringly. The air in the small room was hot and stagnant, and the Ambassador did not sit down. "Plush and the tropics do not go together. They are incompatible," he thought. A discreet cough interrupted his aggressive reflection. The Assistant Chief of Protocol awaited him at the door and with an inclination of his head beckoned him to follow. They passed down a carpeted corridor, where closed doors led to the offices of the President's Councillors, most of them French. They turned left and stopped in front of a high double door. His guide knocked, opened the door, and loudly announced him.

The Ambassador felt a shock—the air-conditioned room was ice cold. The President rose from behind the enormous mahogany desk and walked toward him to shake hands.

He appeared younger and of smaller build than in his pictures. As usual, he was dressed with great attention to detail and without compromise with the climate. His dark gray suit was well cut, the white silk shirt and black tie were perfectly matched. From the

pale gray handkerchief to the handmade shoes, every detail revealed the excellent unobtrusive taste of a cultured gentleman-
intellectual.

The study too was furnished with great taste. The floors were
covered with Persian carpets of a subdued, gray pattern and the
walls with deep-green silk. High, glass-fronted bookcases on one
wall; on another, an exquisite African painting, a composition of
different masks superimposed on a burning-red jungle background. In a corner, a leather ottoman and two heavy armchairs
were placed around a low table. French flowers were everywhere;
one particularly beautiful crystal vase, filled with roses, adorned
the otherwise bare desk. One window was slightly opened, and
the breeze played with the curtain. The only discordant note,
thought the Ambassador, was that stern, official picture of the
Head of State staring from behind his own desk. "The ego guard-
ing the id," he mused.

The President seated his guest on the deep ottoman; he himself
chose the higher armchair. Putting the fingertips of his long,
slender hands together, the ironic smile in his eyes hidden behind
heavy eyeglasses, he said, *"Alors, Monsieur l'Ambassadeur,* what
can I do for you?" For a moment the Ambassador was taken
aback, unsure. But here he was; it had to be tried. . . .

"Mr. President, you may remember I had the honor to attend
your excellent dinner party some two weeks ago, and I tried then
to explain my intellectual predicament to you. At the time, you
most graciously suggested that we pursue our conversation in the
privacy of your study. Needless to say, I am greatly honored and
grateful to your Excellency for this singular favor.

"May I reiterate my problem? The Academy of Social Sciences
of my country has asked me to present a paper on the heritage
left by French and English colonial policies in Africa, and their
political, social, and cultural implications for the future. In an in-
excusable moment of overconfidence, I accepted, and only much
later did I find out that I had to pioneer in an intellectual void. If
there are any serious critical and comparative studies on the subject in the five languages I read, I have been unable to unearth

them. Certainly, there are thousands of books and papers, yet no one seems to have done serious research on the merits or faults of his own nation's attitude or policy as opposed or compared to other colonial powers. Oh yes, they have written lots of nonsense against each other over the last fifty years, but really very little of substance. It seems to me, Mr. President, that there exists a kind of across-the-Channel-conspiracy! Lastly, permit me a personal confession: you know I am accredited to two sovereign African states —one English-speaking, the other French-speaking. Nothing separates those nations on the African level—their people speak the same African tongue, share the same ethnic origin, the same religious beliefs, identical customs, traditions, climates, and soils. But the moment you cross the frontier from one to the other you are in a foreign country. It seems to me that the estrangement between your capital and the neighboring one is deeper than between Paris and London. On the surface, I appreciate the fact that both countries have separate colonial histories lasting for almost four centuries—but what are the implications of these differences for Africa's cultural and political *future*? That is the question I am faced with. In a moment of utter despair I ventured the hope that Your Excellency could help me out of my predicament and straighten out at least some of the complexities."

The President was looking with fascination at his spread-out fingertips. He did not reply for a time. Then he looked sharply at his visitor, straightened up in the chair, put his hands on his knees, and said almost accusingly:

"*Monsieur l'Ambassadeur*, the question you brought before me is complex and loaded. It will have to be broken down into its different components, and each component will have to be analyzed, formulized, and compared, then reintegrated into the puzzleboard of the French and English cultural presence in Africa. As you know, I am the product of French education—I am a French linguist by profession—therefore my reflections on the subject cannot be objective. My knowledge of the English language is rudimentary, my acquaintance with English culture is at best vague and secondhand. All I can do is to try and give you my version as to one-half of your puzzle.

"French language and civilization are the direct and legitimate heirs to classical Roman thought and the doctrines of Latin humanism. Rivarol, in the fifteenth century, said that anything that is not clear is not French. To be clear and to be imbued with reason—this is the basic concept of French humanism through the ages. 'To overcome passions by clear and well-determined judgments—based upon the knowledge of good and bad'—that is how Descartes put it. And French rational thought since, possesses a critical and dialectical quality which enabled France to outgrow its medieval and parochial civilization and develop into a great vehicle for universal humanism in modern times. Already Rabelais and Montaigne preached of ultimate equality among the races. And in the eighteenth century the Revolution's Declaration of Human Rights, speaking of men, meaning all men, led directly to the abolition of slavery in 1794. This French rationalism in its purest form inspired the colonial doctrines that were later on labelled by the catchword 'assimilation.'

"During the four centuries of French colonial expansion and retreat, two antagonistic colonial doctrines clashed—those of assimilation and of association. The doctrine of assimilation was upheld by the progressive forces of French rationalism together with the liberal wing of the French Catholic Church—which is not surprising, since the Church is universal and its message is directed at the human race in its entirety. The doctrine of association was proclaimed by more conservative social and political forces of the day—feudal overlords, merchants, industrialists. The idea had many positive features but never attained the radiance, the humane and intellectual brilliance of the counter-doctrine. I think we may say that it was the more or less veiled credo of French imperial and mercantile interests, and it furnished an easy excuse for irresponsible conquest and often merciless exploitation.

"So you see, the French national genius provided political doctrines and philosophical principles to which their colonized peoples could adhere without losing their personalities or their self-respect. They did not need to be or to become Frenchmen—they only needed to apply French universalist thought and the political ideologies of the day to their own conditions and circumstances, and they would find themselves in the mainstream of European intellectual and political life. The first Negro prince conversing and discussing affairs of state with a European king was Anubia at the court of Louis XIV.

"Please understand me." The President brought his hands together with a clap and continued in an agitated voice. "I do not want either to apologize for the French or to eulogize them. I want to underline an undeniable intellectual fact: one of the mainstreams of French political and social thought during the last three centuries was sufficiently humanistic, rational, and universal to allow the educated African to identify himself with the basic tenets of French culture. The proponents of French rationalism did not always hold political power, but they were powerful enough to assimilate us emotionally and intellectually and to bring us into contact with their civilization. Yes, I do believe in cultural impregnation, in the cross-breeding of civilizations, in the salutary effect of the hybridization of races. For us, mastery of the French language and the possession of French culture were and still are the *sine qua non* for an active African cultural presence on an universal scale. African influence and participation in French culture is an established fact today and has profoundly influenced contemporary French poetry, literature, plastic arts and thought. Assimilation is far from being a one-way street. French culture has been grafted onto the powerful tree of our African civilization. At the same time, our arts and dances, our animistic vitality, rhythm, and mysticism have been grafted onto the venerable tree of French culture. This is not a master-and-slave relationship, but one of cultural equality and reciprocity.

"Some thirty years ago, a few African friends and I launched the cultural movement of the 'African Personality.' Since those days, this concept has been much abused and misunderstood, but a great many African intellectuals nevertheless adhere to it. The philosophy of 'Negroness' is actually the African self-assertion to equal partnership in building Teilhard de Chardin's Civilization of the Universal. After all, it is we—the Africans, the Asians, the Canadians—who give French civilization its global radiance and standing. We are the living propagators of those French values which are truly unique in their humanistic and universal spirit. French culture and civilization needs us in order to accomplish itself; we need French culture to revitalize our African heritage and Negro-African civilization."

The President reclined in his chair, looked questioningly at the Ambassador, and continued.

"As you know, *Monsieur l'Ambassadeur,* I am one of the active supporters—I was even a founder—of an international movement aiming to establish a commonwealth of Francophonic states. Among the 150 million people of the world who speak French as their national or official language, there is much in common. Language is more than a tool; it is a cultural medium and a political reality; it creates and facilitates bonds of rational understanding and common emotional reactions. The Anglo-Saxon world has its own organizational frameworks: the Commonwealth, the Colombo Plan, the British Council, the USIA cultural centers and libraries, the American universities from Beirut to Formosa. Why shouldn't the less powerful, the economically and numerically weaker, French-speaking world cooperate and coordinate its cultural and educational activities, and help its scientific institutions, research laboratories, and universities in one common effort? The Francophonic community will have to prove itself first in education and science. If we succeed there, then we will be able to advance a step further and try to create an international political forum in which all Francophonic nations will be able to voice and harmonize their political positions on the great problems besetting our world. This stage is very far off indeed, but you know that a majority of French-speaking nations, from Laos to Quebec, have already enthusiastically endorsed my ideas on this subject. For reasons of its own, the French Government is still reticent, but this may change soon, I hope. . . . *Hélas,* le Gen-

eral will have to understand once and for all that France's economic and scientific power and wealth are incapable of counter-
balancing the combined resources of the Anglo-Saxon world
alone. France is helping us to develop our educational and scientific institutions at a great sacrifice to herself, but her resources
are limited. We have to appeal to other wealthy French-speaking
peoples—Canadians, Belgians, Swiss—to keep our momentum and
our position."

The President hesitated for a moment as if he wanted to add
another thought, and looked at his visitor over his eyeglasses. The
Ambassador, taking advantage of the breathing spell, said quickly:

"Mr. President, I appreciate your opinions and initiatives on the
questions relating to the French cultural presence in Africa, but
could you perhaps enlighten me on the English contribution in
relation to Francophonic Africa?"

The Head of State put his hands on his knees and smiled
broadly. "In the privacy of my study I will venture some private
opinions. Our English-speaking neighbors and brothers think of
us as snobs who look down our noses at them. (There are many
funny, painful examples. My Minister of Justice, for example,
who represented us in Geneva at an International Conference on
Territorial Waters and Fisheries has studied English for years and
is proud to be able to follow most of the English interventions. He
returned disgusted and told me: 'I understood the Americans
and the English, but the moment an English-speaking African
spoke up, I couldn't understand a word.' He complained bitterly.
'Why didn't the English at least teach them the language? Three
hundred years of British rule—wasn't that long enough?')

"But to return to more serious matters. There is a great difference in the historic motivations that led the two great rival
powers into their colonial adventures. England, as the main naval
power and heir to the Spanish and Dutch colonial empires, obtained the most valuable and the choicest pieces of the lot—the
east coast of North America and Indian subcontinent—and these
were the anchor points of British colonial policy. Africa was for
centuries but a fuelling station on their way to India, a poor, sick

and primitive continent, which, once the slave trade had ceased, was without any serious economic and money-making potential. Still, when the scramble for Africa started, Great Britain participated—almost against her will and certainly against her better business instincts. She was dangerously overextended and involved in many costly local wars.

"The Suez Canal and the gold and diamond discoveries in South Africa changed Britain's political and strategic concept, but not her mercantile attitude toward Africa. It was still the poor orphan, a weak but necessary link to the fabulously rich Indian Empire. So England never furnished Africa with human and material resources in a degree comparable and commensurate with her investment in Asia or the Caribbean. It was simply not worth her while.

"Let me conclude with a personal, subjective generalization: English colonialism was conceived by the merchant and trader class. From the beginning it was a tough, cold economic venture. Only very late, under Queen Victoria, did this change somewhat when the humanizing and civilizing features of education, health, and social services were added. But by that time it was too late. English culture and education came to Africa like an afterthought. There was never any idea of assimilating Africans to metropolitan standards or associating them with it. England ruled pragmatically —and ruled well. She needed low-level African technicians to keep her low-cost, penny-pinching colonial administration efficient, and so she created an educational system adapted to these needs. She ran her African colonies with a minimum of financial investment and manpower—as opposed to the French, who overloaded their colonial administrations with metropolitan Frenchmen.

"Deeper down, it seems to me, the basic difference is one of national psychology. The English character was always strongly clannish, puritanical, and parochial. For him, the world was created by God Almighty exactly as he found it and wanted it to be: with masters and slaves, inferior and superior creeds, classes, nations, and races. Black was black, and white was never white unless it was British. A mixed marriage was unthinkable; social intercourse between one race and the other scandalous. Political power was channeled down from the British regional commissioner through the tribal chiefs imposed on the population by the will and whim of a young British officer. To me, this is the worst service the British rendered us. African tribal and ethnic divisions were archaic and chaotic even before the Europeans arrived, but the British, for the sake of a decentralized, less expensive power structure and administration, froze African social and political evolution for two centuries. To exercise power through the tribal chiefs meant, in reality, to make the most reactionary, corrupt, decadent, and uneducated caste in African society the executors of colonial power. The chiefs were afraid of losing their privileges, and they did more to sabotage modernization and education than their colonial masters. Look at Nigeria and the Congo today. Our great problems are in those regions where the colonial masters reinforced the old tribal hostilities and divisions by means of a decentralized, indirect regional rule.

"The French, on the other hand, organized a highly centralized administration in Africa. Since the time of Louis XIV, the French never conceived of the exercise of executive power differently. I don't think that even the *idea* of decentralized rule crossed the mind of her first colonial governors. For this reason, the French penetration of Africa was always accompanied by bloodshed and armed confrontation. But once and for all, the divisive influence of the reactionary and corrupt class of the tribal potentates was broken and disappeared."

The President stopped suddenly and looked at his watch. "I am sorry, but we have only five minutes left. Let me say just one more thing. The British were tightfisted but just rulers, and they emphasized the gradual economic growth of their possessions. They did not interfere with African traditions and institutions— as long as they did not hamper or counteract British economic interests. The French were harsh conquerors and bad economists, but easy-going and humane colonizers. They never learned to establish a successful colonial economy. Every Governor General arrived with tremendous pomp, and with entirely new ideas and plans to reorganize the colony. First he completely undid everything his predecessor had done; then he started 'his' new projects —roads, schools, industries. Two years later a change of government occurred in Paris, a new Governor General appeared, and the same performance was repeated. They were always obsessed with secondary considerations—national prestige and military pomp. Their swollen administration was ineffective and parasitical. With their great physical courage, their wit, and their silly schemes, they were a rather humane lot, interested in all things African, with that intellectual curiosity peculiar to the French.

"When I was about three or four years old, a French officer came to my parents' compound. My father welcomed him in the courtyard; they shook hands, talked a moment in a language I didn't understand, and then laughed heartily. At that moment I lost forever my fear of the unbaked white man. That was some sixty years ago. Human frailties and errors, together with dedication and courage—these made the Frenchman humane in the eyes of the Africans, and prepared the way for a common future."

Silently, a bemedalled assistant appeared, he too in morning coat and striped trousers, and presented a large silver platter to the President on which a visiting card was placed. The President read the card, looked at his watch, shook his head, and groaned. Getting to his feet, he shook hands warmly with his visitor and showed him to the door. The Ambassador hastily murmured his thanks and appreciation and found himself in the corridor.

"What bit him so suddenly?" he asked himself, walking along the quiet corridor. Two men appeared at its far end walking rapidly toward him. He recognized the Assistant Chief of Protocol and, at his right, yes, certainly, his colleague the Ambassador of France. The French Ambassador stopped, smiled, shook hands, asked some irrelevant questions, then apologized in a conspiratorial voice for having interrupted his audience with the President. "I did not know you were in there. I thought he was having one of his interminable palavers with a marabout or patching up a rift in

the Party or taking care of one of his social cases. Really, I am
sorry. How is he? Has he gotten over his hay fever?" He chatted
amicably for a few minutes and then went on.

The Ambassador passed the guards in deep thought. His beflagged car drove forward. He would love to stay at home tonight
and write down his conversation with the President. But in another two hours he was due at the residence of the Brazilian Ambassador for a dinner party. They would have a *fejoada,* a Brazilian national dish, an excellent but very heavy composition of
dried meat and black beans. . . .

Eight o'clock. Freshly shaven and showered and in his new
tropical white dinner jacket, the Ambassador felt more cheerful,
almost carefree. He turned on the large projector lights around his
house, verified the closed windows and locked doors, and walked
out, locking the front door behind him. He called the night watchman, told him where he was spending the evening, in case of an
unforeseen emergency, and walked down the dark and deserted
street to the Brazilian Ambassador's residence three blocks away.

The ocean breeze was cool and salty, the clear sky covered with
an endless carpet of stars. Only the rhythmic breaking of the
waves and a far away tam-tam could be heard. This was a residential area of private homes surrounded by high-hedged gardens.
Here was Europe in Africa: expensive, luxurious. The Ambassador remembered with a chuckle that he had once offered to his
driver the option of moving with his wife and children into the
Embassy's nice, clean service quarters. The poor fellow was
shocked. "How can I live there without the rest of my family? My
wife would have nobody to talk to." No, Embassy Row was as
foreign to Africa as palm wine to a Frenchman. He walked
through the gate into the Brazilian Embassy's brightly lit garden.

No surprises there—he knew everyone. There were no Africans
present, unless one counted the country's Chief of Staff, General
Jean-Louis Gaye—as French as a general could be, despite the
African blood inherited from his mother. The General was a
jovial, intelligent, outspoken man and a personal friend of the
President's. Since his graduation from a cadet school some forty

years ago, he had diligently served in the French Army. Sometimes, like so many others, on the wrong side, as with General
Pétain. He saw active service around the world. He was in command of a French battalion in southern Germany when the President called him back to organize and head the armed forces of the
newly independent republic.

The Ambassador greeted everyone and took up a strategic
position in a very comfortable easy chair to the left of the Chief
of Staff. General Gaye, a heavy set man whose short steel-gray
hair contrasted attractively with his dark complexion, was involved
in a lively conversation with the wife of the South Vietnamese Ambassador, a delicately beautiful woman of undiscernable age. They
were discussing some Vietnamese dishes of seemingly great gastronomic interest, but after some ten minutes both apparently exhausted the subject. The General turned to the quiet neighbor at
his left. This was the critical moment of the evening. The Ambassador, looking into his glass, told him vaguely, with the proper
undertone of urbane indifference, about his long afternoon audience with the President. The General's professional interest was
immediately aroused, and he wanted to know the why-where-when.
Then he shook his short-cropped head:

"How academic and philosophical—and how unrealistic," he
said. "The facts are so much simpler." He spoke in a low but
intense voice, underlining each sentence with a gesture of his
right hand. "The territorial expansion of French power in Europe
and the conquest of the French Empire were conceived, planned,
and carried out by one body of men, the French Army. You know
as well as I do, the French Army is and always was a virtually
autonomous and powerful establishment within the French body
politic. From the moment that Napoleon conquered Egypt, the
French Army tasted and liked international prestige—the global
strategic importance, and the military and logistic resources that
the newly won colonies offered to it and to France. This did not
change during revolutions, republics, monarchies or empires. It
was the Army that undertook to explore and conquer Africa, and
the Army organized and administered France's colonial territories.

French officers were the first to study and to understand African languages, customs, and mentalities. The French Army was and is a way of life. It always attracted the best human elements of two antagonistic social groups: the feudal and reactionary gentry and, at the same time, the progressive intellectual and liberal forces of the bourgeoisie. Since the Revolution, the French Army has been a people's army: a farmer's son or even a worker's could make a career in it if he had the ability. During the last century the political situation in Paris was often so chaotic that the Army had to take care of its own and safeguard the permanent interests of the French nation, with or without the sanction of the regime of the hour. The Army establishment was and is the guarantor of French aspirations and commitments: national defense, strategic expansion, and the administration of an enormous heterogeneous empire. Officers like Lyautey, Faidherbe, Gallieni, or Brazza were not only the conquerors of the French Empire, but its most liberal, intelligent, and understanding administrators. These men and their officers laid the foundation of common trust and loyalty between the conquerors and the conquered. It was General Faidherbe, a hundred years ago, who introduced peanuts—our only export crop —into our economy. They defended us against the corrupt and rotten commercial concessionary interests which appeared here to exploit our so-called natural wealth. You know, they had the privilege of levying taxes or mobilizing forced labor. In some parts of the interior, like Niger, Ubangi-Shari, and the Congo, the concessionaires depopulated whole regions in the name of some profit-making scheme. Did you know that a 100-mile railway track from Brazzaville to Pointe-Noire cost the lives of 17,000 African workers? This was private enterprise in the colonies!

"The Army knew and understood us—for a simple reason: we were good and loyal soldiers. Yes, the French Army was the first to mobilize Africans into its ranks and to treat them as equals, as soldiers, and the High Command never regretted the decision. No, not the philosophers or the academicians or the Left Bank writers made us what we are today—they arrived on our stage much too late. . . ."

The lady of the house had arrived and stood before them. With a smile she waited until the gesticulating general had perceived her presence. "Please do not get up, particularly as I came to bring you bad tidings. The black beans for my *fejoada* are not done yet; in another ten minutes I will call you. Can I serve you another drink?"

Turning away, she reflected, "Those two will have to be separated. Otherwise they will talk boring African business the whole evening and spoil my party." She smiled at her husband and gestured to him to step aside. They whispered together briefly.

The Ambassador, reminded of the black beans, lifted his hands in submission and murmured, half to himself, half to his neighbor, "Black beans indeed." The General was already talking.

"France's first medical services and public hospitals in Africa were run by the army for its African soldiers and their families, and later for the general public. Our best and largest hospitals even now, eight years after independence, are still run by the army. The first schools were founded for the children of African soldiers. And at the end of the last century and until after World War I, the Army was the main employer in black Africa. During my youth, almost every African family had a relative in the army. During his ten or fifteen years of service, the recruit usually learned to read and write, he often mastered a simple skill or trade, and gained his first experience in civic and national responsibility. It may sound incongruous to you, but African nationalism and independence were born within the first African military units. Service in the army broke the barriers of the insular and reactionary mentality of our rural populations. The army took its recruits from the bush and opened their minds and hearts to the benefits of modern civilization. Whereas the missionaries, the churches, and the public schools concentrated mainly on the population of our cities.

"The French Colonial Army was a thorough, demanding, and often harsh boss. Casualties were always high; many soldiers were maimed or never returned from the overseas campaigns. But there were no color bars: the same uniforms, the same pay, the same conditions for French and Africans alike. When the great tests of African loyalty to France came, in 1914 and 1940, our reaction was instant and emotional. Did you know that in 1945 three-fourths of the Free French Forces under de Gaulle were composed of colonial, mostly African, troops? Even today, the largest and best organized civic organizations in Africa are our veterans. In many of our states they are not only the backbone of civic order and political stability but an important economic force. Our income from veteran pensions is important indeed."

By now General Gaye was sitting on the edge of his chair, his body tense, his eyes excited. An African butler dressed in white, white gloves on his hands, had opened the heavy door leading from the terrace to the dining room, lit with dozens of colored candles. The lady of the house stood in the doorway and called out, "Please do come into the lion's den. It is never too late for dinner."

Conversation ceased, and guests began to get to their feet. The General looked around, somewhat annoyed, and addressed the Ambassador in a loud voice.

"There is a last point I want to make. I hope you do not think me contaminated by professional naïveté. What we need today in Africa are values of a military character—loyalty, dedication, honesty, and sacrifice—because the state of our nations demands it. Look around you, our loud-mouthed politicians are making us the laughing stock of the world! Our administration is rotten to the core, our people are cheated, sacrificed, misguided, and leaderless. The President is a great man, he understands our needs better than anyone else, but he has to compromise with pressure groups and their politicians. Consequently he cannot reach a clear-cut solution to any of the problems affecting our future, but manages only to govern by half-baked decisions. The army is not large now, but we are the only disciplined and effective organization upon whom our President can rely.

"Let me give you some examples: I am setting up and operate agricultural settlements for my veterans in the northeast—after the Ministry of Agriculture failed repeatedly to do so in a sensible

way. Yesterday, the President asked me to take over the organization of the international fair, because it became clear that the
Fair's so-called High Commissioner was incompetent. To spare
us further injury and derision, I accepted and appointed a mayor
to head this military operation, and the first order he gave is self-
explanatory: he appointed a captain and two lieutenants as treas-
urers and paymasters. I am also building and maintaining roads and
bridges. You may ask, where the devil is the public-works department? But nobody knows exactly. . . . The youth organizations
of the country are now my responsibility, too.

"If this process continues, we will arrive at a typical French
impasse: a division of the nation into separate parts, with a parasitical, verbose, and inefficient body of politicians incapable of
action or concerted effort on one side and on the other the military
forces constituting the only group of dedicated, well-organized,
and disciplined men, ready and technically capable of serving their
country.

"The army is here to *serve,* not to govern. That is a French military maxim I accept wholeheartedly. But to serve what? Whom? I
have talked to the President many times about this problem. The
Army men do not want to be the streetsweepers and the menders
of this incapable administration's broken promises.

"So, when you talk about the French spirit, the universality and
humanism of French culture or our assimilation and cultural association with France, I beg you, don't forget that malaria-ridden,
little Auvergnac lieutenant trotting through the bush for weeks
followed by a section of Senegalese tirailleurs. There it all started."

The Ambassador was on his feet. They were alone now on the
terrace. Laughter and babbling voices reached them through the
open dining-room door. He was uncomfortable. Here was a minor
breach of social etiquette: you do not seclude yourself with another guest when invited into the home of a colleague. "General,
let us join the rank and file. Otherwise we won't find anything
left of our promised black beans! . . . Believe me—I am sincerely
grateful for your comments; they are important food for thought.
But one question is nagging me: your young officers who never

served in the French Army, who never lived in France, what is
their state of mind concerning this intimate relationship of inter-
dependence with France?"

The general stopped short, turned toward the Ambassador, and
half-seriously answered, "My friend, as long as I am Chief of Staff,
my attitude and my state of mind are those of the armed forces
of this country." They entered the noisy, candle-lit dining room.

In front of the customs and police shed, a uniformed African
policeman saluted smartly and beckoned the driver to stop. The
Ambassador opened his window. The wind was strong, chasing
heavy, low rainclouds up the river. The policeman had called his
superior, a mustachioed sergeant; this gentleman arrived at a run
jumping over the rain puddles, saluted, clapped his heels like pistol shots, and, from a ten-yard distance, barked: "You Ambassador?" His driver and he both nodded mechanically. "Master Anders say today crossing no good. Much wind. Maybe come back
tomorrow?" He again saluted with pistol shots, turned about, and
returned quickly to his shed.

The Ambassador was too astonished to say anything. He looked
at the sergeant's smart retreating figure—the rolled-up blue socks,
the boots shining like mirrors, the newly laundered knife-creased
khaki shorts, khaki sweater, and the dark blue cap. Annoyed, he
told his driver to follow the sergeant and tell him that the Ambassador was angry. He had driven for six dreary hours to this
crossing point, and he intended to cross—wind or no wind. Where
was his promised launch? Here or still at the other shore? The
excited driver ran toward the police station, jumping over the
muddy rain puddles, and disappeared inside the shed.

The wide cement jetty was deserted. White capped waves
broke loudly and flooded over the jetty with their foaming spray.
The ocean breeze was still strong. The river was twelve miles wide
at this point, actually more of an ocean inlet than a river mouth.
This was a border station between the two African nations where
the Ambassador represented his country. The two states were as
different from each other as states can be, but both had been

founded 350 years ago as trading and slaving posts for European powers, and both were populated by the same ethnic and linguistic African groups.

The driver returned. He had spoken with the sergeant in the local dialect, he said, his white teeth flashing, and had been informed that the government launch had been waiting here for two hours—long before the wind interrupted the river traffic. Mr. Anders *had* phoned, but the decision to cross or not had been left entirely with the Ambassador.

They drove down the jetty, pointing like a thin finger into the ocean. There below, on the sheltered side, they found the shabby, old, twenty-foot diesel launch tied up against some deserted crafts filled with sacks of peanuts. Two sailors appeared and helped the Ambassador climb over the other boats. Both looked preoccupied and tense. The older one went to the wheel while the younger busied himself with the motor, which stuttered suddenly to life. The young sailor brought in the ropes. The Ambassador sat in the little aft cabin with his suitcase at his side. At his feet, the open motor hammered and smoked away. With his foot, he cleaned away a little greased square shield on the motor's edge: here was written, in formerly gilded letters, "Constructed and built in Portsmouth 1931." The two sailors called out to each other over the motor's noise, and the launch began to move slowly sideways and then forward. After a few minutes it lurched violently, like a wounded animal, and sea water poured through the door into the cabin.

The Ambassador remembered that during the same kind of weather only a few years ago, the big ferryboat, a remodeled World War II landing craft, had sunk like a stone with 157 people on board. He decided to leave the smelly and creaking cabin and lifted himself onto the lurching and moving deck. A strong wind blew spray all over the little craft. Nothing could be seen but deep, white-crested waves and the leaden, low sky. A crosswave thundered against the hull. The launch shivered and groaned; this must be the midstream of the inlet. Wave after wave thundered against the launch's side. Then, equally suddenly, the movement abated. They had entered the protected waters of the other shore.

Another ten minutes and the launch coasted into the large government pier at the southern bank. The Ambassador later told his friends he had been so frightened that he had simply no time to be ill, and motors built in Portsmouth in 1931 had gained considerable prestige. The two sailors smiled broadly at their passenger—all three soaking wet from head to foot. The Ambassador thanked both of them profusely and gave them each a large tip. They had earned it.

On the pier, a few dozen Africans sat shivering on their bundles, their long boubous drawn over their heads, waiting for the ferryboat. An old, black Humber made its way carefully toward the edge of the pier and stopped nearby. Out stepped Anders, the country's Foreign Office Chief of Protocol, Secretary General, Chief of Cabinet—in short, its man for all seasons and occasions. Anders, a mulatto, brought intelligence, affability, and a capacity for organization to his work—and these qualities showed now. Apologizing for the weather, he inquired anxiously about the crossing and then produced from his breastpocket a typewritten working schedule for the next two days: Dinner tonight with the Governor General; working sessions tomorrow morning with the Ministers of Agriculture, Finance, and Education; lunch with the Prime Minister. They entered the driveway leading to the hotel. The Ambassador had two hours to himself—to rest, shower, and dress.

The Governor General's twenty-five-year-old Rolls Royce arrived silently, exactly five minutes ahead of time, to pick up the Ambassador. It would not take more than three minutes to drive the half-mile to the mansion. Here, not as in the other capital, the streets were dark and deserted. The low white-washed buildings facing the main street looked poor and of uncertain craftsmanship. On the corner, two high-gabled churches faced each other: the Cathedral of the Church of England and the Methodist Church were as British as any edifices could be. They passed by the town green, a large, fenced-in square in the center of the city used for military parades of the 250-man army and for cricket matches. Under the few street lights along the road, groups of teen-age boys sat reading their school books or writing busily in notebooks on their knees. These were the pupils of the country's only high school preparing for their lessons and exams. Electricity was expensive here—few Africans could afford it—and the street lamps were important.

The Governor General's garden was one of the most beautiful and well-kept on the west coast of Africa. For more than a hundred years, the British governors and their wives had made this park their hobby and pride. Here were age-old jacaranda trees, limes, oranges, and dozens of different acacia species planted in profusion on the cropped lawns. The mansion itself was a massive structure built about 150 years ago for an English admiral commanding the coastal navy station. Its high, narrow windows and doors gave the place an austere, fortress-like character. Venerable navy cannons ornamented the short driveway to its entrance.

The Governor General's British private secretary was in attendance and requested the Ambassador to sign his name in the heavy guest book—a custom, it seems, retained since the days of the naval commander's logbook. He found Lady Roberts in the living room, talking to two elderly African ladies clothed in too-tight European dresses. Lady Roberts greeted the ambassador smilingly and gave him a powerful handshake. She was a stately, well-rounded woman in her early fifties, with the blue eyes and the lovely outdoor complexion of a British sportswoman. She wore her gray hair in a simple chignon low on her neck and no jewelry at all.

"I am glad to see you, Mr. Ambassador, really I am. I need someone capable of telling me what is going on in the world. Do you know—I haven't read a newspaper for the last three months! The *Times* not only arrives irregularly, but often it's weeks late. That makes reading it a very frustrating experience. So tonight you must bring me up to date on what's going on in this world of ours. But please meet my charity committee; we are preparing our next church bazaar."

"Your Excellency, don't . . . ," boomed Sir Christopher's deep voice. The Governor General, coming in from the terrace, was a powerfully built man with the broad shoulders of a sportsman and the erect posture of a professional officer. His dinner jacket was of an old cut, but fitted him admirably well. Sir Christopher had already served thirty-five years in the Colonial Service.

"I understand you had a rough crossing this afternoon." Sir Christopher turned to his wife. "Do you know why the Ambassador endangered our only government launch? He didn't want to miss one of your famous dinners."

Lady Roberts laughed. "That is only human. After all, how long can one suffer that heavy, saucy French cuisine without succumbing to some beastly liver ailment?"

Sir Christopher looked at his watch. "We still have forty minutes until dinner. Let us retreat from the ladies to my study. We can have a drink there and talk for a while."

Sir Christopher's little study was simply furnished, almost austere: a wide hardwood writing desk, a few very comfortable deep leather armchairs. Its white walls were hung with rare old etchings of the West African coast and the originals of some treaties signed 300 years ago by African chiefs, renting or loaning coastal land to forgotten British sea captains. The study breathed the no-nonsense atmosphere of a far-flung empire, and its lack of ostentation was more impressive than a display of riches and luxury. An African butler came in to serve the whisky. Sir Christopher lit his pipe and the Ambassador a cigarette. They talked briefly about the political situation in the country, peanut prices and harvest, and the few technical assistance projects the Ambassador's country supported. Their relaxed conversation touched as usual, upon problems of the neighboring French-speaking country: its government, its liking for impressive state functions somehow out of proportion to its means. The newly built, air-conditioned state theater seating 1200 was a case in point—it had cost $2 million and operated for only thirty or forty nights a year, mostly for state functions. The Governor commented on the main highway neon lighting system from the town to the airport, entirely imported from France with its beautifully curved tall cast-iron lampposts, giving the coastal city the air of an elegant Riviera beach—at the cost of half a million dollars. "It's incredible—how can one do such things and at the same time talk about austerity, national mobilization for economic development, war on illiteracy, illness, and corruption? Besides, it's political dynamite. The French in Africa have left them all their faults and none of their virtues," Sir Christopher remarked.

The Ambassador felt the moment was propitious to bring up the subject of his special interest. He told the Governor General about his conversation with the President on the subject of the heritages left by 350 years of French and British colonial rule and their possible implications for Africa's future.

The Governor General cleaned his pipe, then sat back in his chair and said humorously, "You want me to appear on your panel as a defender of the British colonial record? You will be surprised: I am ready. Three centuries ago our Kings and lords gambled their money away on hearsay mountains of gold and entrusted unsavory adventurers with the command of ships and men. The motivations for colonial acquisitions in those days were simple and straightforward: the lust for gold and sheer, crude power. Our forefathers may have been blackguards, but at least they were not hypocrites. Still, I can't excuse or explain away the historical calamity of slavery. For two centuries the slave trade, and the moral depravity it engendered, was officially sanctioned. We have nothing to be proud of—we all owe the black man an enormous moral and human debt, and we shall never be able to undo the misdeeds of our forebears.

"Having said this, I want you to know that in England, too, we had a few pious dissenters—philosophers, intellectuals, clergymen —fighting against the rapaciousness of their time. Neither Rabelais nor Hume had any direct influence upon political events; neither had Descartes nor Locke. I simply do not accept the need to rewrite history whenever we feel the need to apologize for past misdeeds. Why should we defend a black historical record behind high-sounding but empty historical doctrines and dishonest definitions? Would it not be more appropriate, before citing Rabelais or Chaucer, to quote the Sermon on the Mount or Saint Augustine and send all our forefathers to Dante's hell? In one sentence: I cannot defend the record of our colonial history of these 200 years, and nobody asked me to apologize for the sins of my forefathers."

The Governor looked across the room at an old etching of a British man-of-war on the high sea, firing a full broadside at an unseen enemy. He sucked at his pipe pensively.

"Certainly, someone else would defend the British record by retelling the great words and deeds of a few far-sighted and courageous Englishmen—intellectuals, clerics, and soldiers—who fought with their own weapons against the inhumanities of their time. In 1760, Philip Quaco, a Negro from the Cape Coast, was ordained in Oxford and became the first African bishop of the Anglican church. And the name of Wilberforce will always shine in this context. We mustn't forget, either, that Wilberforce was the leader of a large and powerful segment of British public opinion of his day. It is quite true, the abolition of slavery decreed in the French Revolution preceded the English abolition by a decade. But the fact of the matter is that the French abolition was never effective, because Napoleon reintroduced and legalized slavery barely ten years after its abolition had been lauded as one of the great contributions to the cause of human freedom. It was the *British* Navy which fought alone for two long decades to break up the traffic. Only much later did the American and French join us in this action.

"The key to the matter, it seems to me, lies in the differences in national character and temperament. We British take our time to pass a law—but once decreed, we adhere to it. The French are the great masters of words—their realization and their consequences in the life of men and nations seem of only secondary concern. The realities of colonial rule were never influenced by philosophical doctrines like Assimilation or Association or by catchword expressions like 'British paternalism' or 'mercantilism.' Not doctrines, but national interests dictated colonial policies.

There is more in common between Rhodes and Luggard, Lyautey and Faidherbe than between their respective biographers and historians. The conquerors and founders of the two empires had similar, if not identical, strategic concepts and national and economic motivations. Only history is not made in the field, but in the manuals of public schools."

The Governor pointed the stem of his pipe at the Ambassador, underlining each word.

"Look at the British record of the last century. We are dealing now with facts and figures, not oratory. The illiteracy rate in former British colonies is lower than in the former French possessions. There are more doctors and hospital beds per head and more public schools and universities relative to the mass of population in English-speaking Africa. I do not accept the validity of the argument that British Africa was economically better endowed, more densely populated, and had better natural internal lines of communication. This is a fallacy. There was little difference in the natural resources or mineral wealth of countries like Ghana and the Ivory Coast, or of the Cameroons compared to Nigeria, or poor-rich Gabon with rich-poor Sierra Leone. You have to recognize these facts. They cannot be talked away. At independence, Ghana had a yearly per capita income of $200; the Ivory Coast, $100. The illiteracy rate in the Ivory Coast was 95 per cent, in Ghana, 75 per cent. Just recently I discovered another interesting fact: In 1965, at Ibadan University in Nigeria, one-third of the professors were Africans, while at the much older university in Dakar, I don't know if Africans accounted even for 5 per cent of the teaching staff."

"Sir," interrupted the Ambassador, aware that the evening was drawing to a close. "Please give me the benefit of your thought: How will the British heritage influence Africa's future, as compared to the French?"

The Governor General smiled and sucked at his cold pipe. "I'm afraid that food, oratory, and amenities of life will always be superior among our French-speaking neighbors. Nevertheless, in economics, in agricultural and industrial development, we are leaving

behind a sound structure adapted to Africa's potentials and based
on economic and human realities. We are leaving behind solid
economic foundations and an efficient, well-trained public administration which has proven its worth—by African standards. I mean,
we bequeathed a solid tradition of realism in economics and pragmatic solutions in politics. Each territory should be self-supporting.
France always pumped huge subsidies into her colonies. Even
today most French-speaking states still depend on France to balance their budgets. This French policy, creating an artificially
high living standard in the cities, has resulted in enormous internal tensions and political difficulties. Our former colonies may
look poorer, but in reality their economics are basically sounder
and they are more independent of foreign charity and its related
political pressures. Ours has been a penny-pinching approach, but,
I think, as time goes by African leaders will appreciate the merits
of this peculiarity of our national character.

"We never intended to make Englishmen out of Africans, but
we tried to equip the African with the most important accessories
of European civilization and technology. He went to our schools
—he has been taught all we know which we think can be of use
to him. If he needs us still for specialized vocations, for professional counsel—we will help him as much as we can. But from
Independence day on, he is responsible for all his sins of commis-
sion and omission.

"The character of our relationship will be determined by fundamental national interests—not by suave ideologies. Africa will buy
British goods as long as they are reasonably priced and of good
quality; if not, we have taught him to bargain hard and get his
supplies from other sources. In fact, exports from Britain to
its former colonies have declined considerably since independence,
and our exporters do compete hard for formerly secure markets.
That, too, is part of the British way of accepting a new reality.
Most African nations have chosen a republican system of government and sooner or later have dissolved their special relationship
to the Crown. At the time, we were disturbed by the hasty change
of constitutions: Yes, we felt doubts and emotional misgivings

about their precipitate action, and, I am sorry to say, they were only too justified. Since once the constitution was changed, most African republics became disguised autocracies—little dictatorships or one-party states. But we never intervened, either directly or indirectly. The way to statehood is long and tortuous. The responsibilities are theirs, and theirs alone.

"Also, I am glad to say, there is much less official ostentation and squandering of meager public resources in English Africa than in French Africa. We have left behind a reasonable scale of public values, anchored upon the primacy of law—the superiority of hard facts as against the allure of fictions. The members of the British Commonwealth of Nations are not birds of a feather —far from it. But our African friends have found their place there and none has expressed a wish to leave our venerable club."

There was a discreet knock at the door. The Governor got out of his armchair, looked at his watch. "We are late, but let me give you my version of the question of culture and language." He stood up straight in the middle of the room. His light blue eyes took on a remote and icy expression.

"Neither French nor English are African languages. Africans are welcome to use one or both. If East Africans choose Swahili as their official language, as they will sooner or later, it will be because Swahili is an indigenous African language, expressing the African personality infinitely better than any imported idiom. Black Africa will use English or French as necessary instruments for bringing modern technology and science into a badly underdeveloped continent. And as long as England and the United States will be the great powers they are today, English will be spoken all over the world, because our technological civilization and industrial power are superior to others. It is a fallacy to believe that Chaucer, Shakespeare or Milton can only be understood in their original versions. The translations of Dostoevsky and Chekov influenced occidental literature and theater more than Balzac or G. B. Shaw. But the cultural contribution of Africa will be typically African in content and form, not a mimicry or secondhand copy of European originals. On this point, I accuse our

French neighbors of having enticed their African friends into the well-known fold of French intellectual chauvinism and arrogánce —turned them into black parochial French nationalists of a strange sort. But Africa hasn't the potentiality of becoming a Quebec, and French acculturation is a great political obstacle in the unification of the continent."

The door opened. Lady Roberts entered shaking her head. "What have you two been up to? What secrets kept you away from your guests? I hope you didn't concoct anything that will interfere with our home leave."

The dinner was a formal, candlelit affair. The Ambassador was seated between Lady Roberts and Mrs. Laye, the wife of the African Prime Minister. The French wines were excellent: '57 Montrachet and '59 Chateau Lafite. But the food was unidentifiable, overcooked and underspiced as usual. The roast beef was the Ambassador's undoing. Talking with Mrs. Laye, he had forked a good-sized piece into his mouth without prior inspection. Now, he chewed and chewed with mounting anxiety, but the beef was stubborn, forming a kind of flexible, rubbery ball in his mouth. What does one do? To spit it out was impossible. It would be scandalous, the hostess sitting at your right. To swallow it was impossible. The next five minutes passed and the Ambassador was still chewing hard on his roasted rubber ball; cheekbones and muscles ached. Lady Roberts turned to him gaily. "Please tell us, how do you live across the river for months on end, in social turmoil and eating heavy French food, without falling to pieces?" The Ambassador made a momentous decision. He stopped chewing, took a big swig of Chateau Lafite and with an enormous effort swallowed the rubber ball. He felt it going down, scratching here, bouncing there, but down it went. He breathed deeply. "Madame, we diplomats are the unsung heroes of many unknown sacrifices and heroic deeds."

Dinner finished, the ladies withdrew to the living room and the men followed the Governor General into his study. Laughing loudly like a schoolboy, he questioned: "Does anyone wish to follow me into the garden to see the flowers growing in the tropical moonlight?" The Ambassador declined; he did not feel romantic enough for the task. The Governor General, the Prime Minister, the Chief Justice, and the Minister for Local Government trooped out into the garden—to relieve themselves. This was an old, venerable custom here. What plumbing existed in the old buildings was reserved for the ladies. The men went outdoors. "What happens during a rainstorm?" mused the Ambassador. "Will we have to use Elizabethan chamberpots?"

All the men were comfortably seated in deep armchairs, brandy in hand, cigars smoking. With a twinkle in his eyes for the Ambassador, the Governor General stated in a few sentences the subject of their pre-dinner conversation. "Gentlemen, the floor is yours. Please let us have your opinions."

For a moment there was deep silence in the room. Then the Prime Minister coughed lightly—a well-known sign that he was prepared to speak. He was fortyish, a veterinarian by profession, a capable, intelligent, and introverted person who took himself and his public office very seriously. He was a hard political campaigner and an excellent administrator, and he had succeeded in amalgamating a majority party from different tribal and religious groups. He put his brandy glass on a low table, puffed at his cigar, and began to speak in a low voice.

"It is all very confusing, I must say, especially to simple spirits like ours. We don't speak French, they don't speak English, but we talk in our own African language. It has its disadvantages because it was never constructed to deal with modern affairs of state, but we manage. Nevertheless, every time I come home from across the river, I ask myself if I have not returned from Alice's wonderland. Our common problems are technically simple—they are all centered on our common border, the river. Here a few miles of asphalted road have to be added; there we have to find money for a new ferryboat. All this presents few difficulties. But the *way* it is done—that is so perplexing. For us, five miles of road means expenses and revenues. To our brethren it means international and inter-African communications, African unity, and world brotherhood. This is all very frustrating because I am simply interested in asphalting five miles of road and in buying a second-hand ferryboat.

"Needless to say, our meeting doesn't decide anything, road or boat. A long communiqué is issued and the meeting is adjourned for months. Is that the French way of transacting business?

"Another matter bothers me. Both our countries are agriculturally poor. We have no mineral wealth to speak of. But look on either side of the river. Here we live like the paupers we are and we try to balance our budget. We have 250 soldiers in all. On the other side—stadiums, theaters, hotels, beaches, restaurants, international conferences and festivals, 40,000 government employees, 7,000 soldiers. Our people must ask themselves sooner or later what is wrong. Why do we have to live in misery with a balanced budget if our neighbors live so much better with an unbalanced one?"

The Prime Minister put his brandy glass aside and lit a new cigar. He looked across at the Ambassador.

"Every time I go across the river, I ask myself in despair, 'What price independence?' Each time there is a new voguish intellectual affair occupying the administration to the exclusion of everything else. Two years ago they discussed 'African socialism'—its definition, content, form, application. Last year, 'the specifics of the African personality' was the topic of the day. Last week the administration was organizing an international seminar on 'the African contribution to universal arts.' That international seminar is not a seminar at all—it is a little U.N. conference. Some thirty states have already announced their participation. The French are sending a delegation headed by a minister and are paying most of the hotel, travel, and organizational expenses involved. More money is being contributed by an American foundation, and, I'm afraid it does not exactly know what it is all about. There will be white-tie dinners and black-tie receptions, official galas at the stadium, theater premieres, a special exhibit at the museum, and days and days of speech-making. I mean, after all, what is the importance of Vietnam, Czechoslovakia, or Biafra? You realize by now that as a good neighbor, I will play my part and address the gathering. I dislike pretentiousness, but what can one do?

"At the same time, there are all sorts of other problems, less interesting but real ones. Take, for instance, our agricultural producer cooperatives. In the last five years, ours made a very decent profit, theirs went into debt—they had the wrong concept, they mismanaged it, and their administration was incapable and corrupt. I suggested to their President that possibly the British do not know much about culture and civilization, but they do know how to make whisky and how to run a cooperative. Why not ask for an English team to reorganize their Central Cooperative Administration on our efficient, modern lines? The President did not refuse, but he sounded doubtful. Unluckily, the issue has international ramifications. Their farmers and herders feel cheated by their cooperatives, they are not paid in cash so they smuggle thousands of tons of produce into our country and sell it cheaply to our farmers, their relatives, who in turn sell it with their own yield to *our* cooperatives against cash. Their farmers would have gotten much better prices in their own market, but this way they are recompensed by purchasing rice, cloth, cigarettes, transistors —which they can buy here much more cheaply without paying the 100 or 200 per cent import tax levied in their own country.

"Now they want us to stop that traffic—with army units patrolling the border, the police requisitioning villages and arresting all offenders. I told them, 'My friends, that is your problem, not ours. Reorganize your cooperatives on efficient and profit-making lines, and no one will be happier than your farmers!'

"Every time I come home, I need time to readjust to realities. I may never learn to understand them, but, frankly, I am always happy to come back to an Africa I know and understand."

The butler filled their glasses from a heavy crystal decanter. The Prime Minister kept quiet and sipped his drink. The Minister for Local Government, Samba Tall, now started to speak. He was the youngest member of the group, descended from an influential family of chiefs up-river; who had studied law in England and the United States—a quiet person, hard to know.

"My family has lived for centuries on both sides of the river. Therefore, I have some personal experience and am familiar with the issue.

"Our French-speaking brothers are excellent and courteous hosts—they are good neighbors. Their hospitality is so overwhelming that we often come home with a bad conscience, since we are incapable of reciprocating measure for measure.

"Maybe the French language plays an important part in our misunderstandings? Is it possible that in French, their acts and behavior make sense in a way we fail to understand in English or in African languages? It seems to me that everything we said tonight touches only one side of the coin. Whom are we talking about? Only 10 per cent of them—the urban elite, the intellectuals, the administration, the French and foreign colonies in the capital. Ninety per cent of their population is as poor as ours, and have no interest or understanding of the capital. They have the same beliefs, customs, and traditions, speak the same language, and are faced with the same agricultural problems. So our differences lie in our capitals and in the mentality of our elites, not in the country. Across the border the French succeeded in breeding an exclusive, symbiotic elite of French-Africans—an intelligent, well-educated, charming, highly cultivated, sensitive lot, but they are not entirely at home or at ease here. They do not fit into today's Africa.

"The British proceeded differently. They were mainly interested in the formation of low- and middle-level technicians, able to assist the British officers and possibly to replace them—in due time. The British colonial administration abhorred all things intellectual in general, and the intellectual native son in particular —they were potential troublemakers and rabble-rousers. In reality, British colonial policy was not only reactionary, but anti-intellectual. With your kind permission, Sir Christopher, may I say that the British colonial establishment never considered the formation of an indigenous elite—in addition to the natural elite of chiefs and elders—as politically expedient or even desirable. Ironically, the British bias against the formation of an Anglo-African intelligentsia has had many advantages. Since the British administration neither minded nor cared about our internal African cultural and social affairs, we were able to develop an intellectual elite of greater cohesiveness. It grew in common with our social structures and needs—it was never imposed upon us from outside. It never cut itself off from the social and political mainstream of our people.

"We are all governed by the elites we merit. But our neighbor's elite is not the product of their own national evolution. It was tele-commanded from abroad. How long can that go on? It is a matter for some anxiety, because their troubles will be ours, and our destinies are bound together. What has the future in store for us? Is the French-African elite the residue of a cultural imperialism; is it an artificial transplant of European culture to Africa—and therefore doomed to failure; or is it the symbol and forerunner of our future, the pioneers of a detribalized, literate, industrialized African society?"

The door opened, and Lady Roberts invited the gentlemen to join the ladies in the living room. A half hour later, at 11 o'clock sharp, the guests departed.

In the privacy of his hotel room, clad in his pajamas, the Ambassador wrote in his diary for almost an hour. Before closing his notebook, he jotted down a phrase from *Hamlet* that seemed an appropriate motto to conclude the evening:

"Things standing thus unknown shall live behind me."

FIVE

The Ambassador's Diary

JANUARY 14

F INALLY. THE MINISTER'S CABLE CONFIRMING MY transfer came yesterday. For a year, I have been asking for it, I expected it, and now it is here, under my eyes. But contrary to all reason, a feeling of loss and guilt persists, as if I had been engaged in a competition and lost, as if I were leaving unfulfilled promises or deserting friends in need.

But a professional like me should be uninvolved. My assessments and opinions should be coldly objective, entirely nonpersonal. Yet Africa's problems are so immense, so dramatically human—they simply do not conform to a conventional diplomatic norm. Once you become involved, even unwillingly, they persist in your mind like a haunting nightmare. *Why?* Why do I (and many of my colleagues) feel so involved in and attracted by this uncomfortable dark continent? Really—I have fallen short of the Palmerston-Talleyrand concept of a diplomat.

Looking through my African library, I sense with frustration that the studies and researches I collected so diligently, catalogued with so much care, and read so avidly, have been of little use. Only very few of the books are of permanent value; most were already obsolete at the time of their publication. The political geographies, the historical and anthropological studies, the analyses by economists and political scientists are remote from reality and fall short of facts and events. Far from the depressing realities, it is easy to be clever and sophisticated. I should not be so harsh in my criticism, since most of them are really academic experiments and were never intended to be brought face to face with African reality. They are of little relevance to the "men in the field" who desperately need information and reliable technological knowledge. Let's admit it clearly, most Western aid and assistance was given or denied on some sort of intuition—we preferred to call it "African experience"—a faulty basis of judgment, but used by men who tried their best and were ready to learn from their failures.

In a few weeks' time, all my exertions, all my intellectual and emotional involvement with Africa's economic and human problems will become dormant and obsolete—a fading memory. But I *must* try to remember the lessons I have learned. I must put them down now, while impressions are still vivid and my brain is geared to the task and not yet weighted down by the complexities of a new assignment. It is a kind of challenge—a private feat I want to accomplish: to sum up my personal impressions of the obstacles confronting Africa's entry into the modern world. These obstacles are twofold: those created by nature and others invented by men. Otherwise my modest canvass will be off balance and misunderstood.

JANUARY 15

Remember ten years ago, on the eve of African independence, the boundless enthusiasm, the great hopes, the tremendous challenges! Africa was at the center of public attention and appeared on the front pages for years. Western governments competed in launching assistance projects. Private firms cautiously moved in, probing here, investing there. International organizations spread

their network of institutions and projects over the whole continent. Engineers, agronomists, economists, and sociologists fought
over fine points in their relevant papers. All was movement and
excitement! Answers were plentiful: three-year plans, five-year
plans, experimental stations, regional development plans, new
universities, international conferences, official visits by the score,
new political ideas, and regional and continental cooperation
schemes, all appeared on the scene at once.

Today all that has changed. African exuberance has given way
to resigned despair. Foreign governments are cautious—their aid
budgets are trimmed year after year. The international organizations still have large staffs here, but their over-weighted bureau-
cracy and lack of investment funds limit their efficiency.

So, the mountain brought forth a mouse. As an example, our
cherished resettlement scheme. My predecessor and I enthusiastically endorsed the project, and we planned, built, and equipped
two model villages for specially trained African settlers. Its phased
realization was supervised by dedicated European technicians. At
the beginning everything was successful and everyone was enthu-
siastic. Then after three years of incessant work and almost two
million dollars of investment, difficulties appeared. The model
settlements, once turned over to the settlers, reverted to typical
traditional African villages—neither better nor worse. Innovations
were abandoned—the lucrative new crops left for the old ones, the
collective effort necessary for irrigated cultivation given up for the
individual extensive subsistence agriculture of old. Machinery lay
idle and unrepaired, and even the marketing cooperative ceased
activity.

Our sociologist denounced the passivity of the farmers and the
paralyzing effect of African traditionalism as the main reason for
failure. Our agronomists told me about the Africans' lack of interest in his work—their lack of inventiveness and resistance to
modern methods. The economist explains not only that the lack
of more investment capital made for difficulties in the project, but
also the latent rural animosity against all forms of modernization
and change. The most appropriate and intelligent remark came

from the head of our agricultural team: "With better educated and better qualified farmers we could have succeeded—technically —but the model villages would never have developed their own momentum. They were another White Man's experiment, foreign to the African rural scene."

JANUARY 16

A few weeks ago I spent a day in these model villages, talking to the farmers. I went alone, without a technician. The settlers are a friendly, hospitable lot—known to me for many years. In their eyes I am their foreign benefactor. They regretted keenly my disappointment in our experiment.

The farmers criticized their modern cement-block houses—they are too cold in winter and too hot in summer. And they still resent the fact that during the settlement period, when they lacked the bare necessities of life, we constructed these expensive dwellings, costing ten times more than the traditional mudbrick ones. The houses were also too small for their large families, they claimed, and they had to build additional quarters. The cement structures are now used mostly for storage and as work sheds.

When I asked them why the teacher employed to instruct the adults, had left the village, the settlers' answer was simple: "If the government wants us to spend two hours a day studying, then the government should pay us for the time lost from work." Apparently, they do not accept the need for literacy. For their children, however, schooling is considered highly desirable and necessary.

The simple tools which had been given to each family were in a bad state of repair or unusable. The settlers claim that they requested repairs and spare parts, but that the government did not provide either at a reasonable price. The government also had not sent the promised tractor for clearing and ploughing the newly reclaimed fields. It was, it seems, undergoing endless repairs in the regional capital.

My inquiry about the breakdown in the collective working

schedule in the irrigated fields, and the abandonment of the new cash crops, was time-consuming but highly informative. The irrigation system consisted of a pumping station and an intricate network of earth canals channeling the water into the fields. If not constantly watched and repaired, water breaks out easily, flooding fields and destroying large sections of the canal system—which has to be rebuilt patiently and quickly after each irrigation. During the hot season, this system demands night shifts, and it generally imposes a radical change in working attitudes. Tensions developed among individuals and family groups in which the African government technicians assigned to the project took an active part. Accusations and counteraccusations reached the danger point of physical violence. During these weeks, irrigation ceased entirely. Then the quarrelsome technicians departed, and the settlers distributed the collective fields among themselves and each started to exploit his own plot. Meanwhile, the pumping station had stopped working and needed to be repaired. The farmers seemed relieved by the disappearance of the feud and the return to the old, well-known order. It was a situation they understood and could handle themselves. They were cheerful and optimistic.

It became clear to me that the novel ideas of intensive agriculture, collective labor effort, new crops, and new working implements were regarded as impositions. As long as the villagers were paid daily wages, no one minded. But on their own, the group could not understand the meaning of the project as a whole, and could not conform to its unfamiliar requirements. Three years of preparation and visual education by our technicians had done little to change the ingrained attitudes. Certainly they learned to appreciate the tractor and the plough, and how to prepare a field before and after sowing. They even asked me to send one of our European technicians back—to repair the pump, to bring the tractor, and to help them market their produce. And they were proud of their relative achievements. They felt more advanced and better equipped than the other villages near by. But when I asked if they regretted the over-all failure of the modernizing project, their spokesman told me, "No. Model villages are good for the White Man. He does things we cannot do: we do things he cannot do."

We parted good friends. I will find ways and means to help them, maybe with seeds, fertilizers, and some simple equipment, and even with their broken pump and the lost tractor. But one conclusion is obvious: the project failed because it was imposed on the settlers. We approached the matter with a more or less authoritarian technological thoroughness. We did not take account of the communal mentality of the villages, but aimed at the profit motive of the individual peasant. It was, I think, a fateful choice. We considered the individual as the basic unit of our development project. To him we gave seeds and implements, and to him we tried to give education and inspiration. The village community as such was not allowed to confront development, which is primarily concerned with efficiency. We instinctively distrusted its traditional antagonism and rancor.

Why did we not inform the community about our plans? Why were the villagers not asked if they wanted or needed those houses? Why were they not informed about the cost of the literacy project, and why were they not asked if they wanted the funds to be used in that way? Why were they not consulted about the introduction of new crops and seeds? Their questions should have received honest answers, leaving the door open to remarks and criticisms.

In other words, our patronizing posture and the African government's authoritarian attitudes should both be abandoned. They are ineffective policies. We should have given the settlers an opportunity to express their opinion freely at each stage. Prior to the establishment of a small, elected executive body, a consultative public body seems indispensable. It should be consulted on all matters of regional concern, and it should be given all the necessary information. It should have the right to suggest, criticize, and accuse. At first, debates in such an assembly will be confused and time-consuming, but they would have an over-all educational value. They would give us a true picture of the social obstructions we confront and will permit our technicians to learn how to deal

with them. In listening to objections and criticisms, they will be
forced to think through their plans again and adapt and modify
them.

Only if the village community can be induced to form a public
opinion on the issues affecting their lives, will we be able to plant
the seed of progress. We will have to adapt ourselves to a slower
and more gradual process of modernization. There are no short
cuts.

JANUARY 18

Centers of human civilization developed in easily accessible
geographical regions. The Nile and Euphrates valleys, the broken
coastlines of Greece and Italy, the river systems of Western Europe and its many natural harbors and wide open expanses were
and still are centers and nerve lines of communication. The great
civilizations of old and the powerful cultural and political units
of today all depended on a continuous interchange of material
and on cultural intercommunications.

Africa's communication with the outside has been extremely
difficult and hazardous because of its closed natural configuration
(except along the Mediterranean coast), its harsh climate, its
deserts, and its tropical forests. The great deserts in the north
and south did not impede the interchange of material and ideas
within Africa, but they certainly have not facilitated it. The continental river system is notoriously difficult and often unnavigable.
The fluctuation of the water level is great: a roaring river may
dry out in a short period of time. Most rivers have falls and rapids,
and many of their outlets to the sea are hopelessly sandy, and im-
penetrable. The endemic illnesses—like malaria, bilharziasis,
sleeping sickness, leprosy, typhoid fever—have their own slowing-
down effect on human society in Africa. And the climate is
extreme: long, hot, rainless months; then torrential downpours
during the rainy season. Near the equator, incessant rainfall with
high temperatures render agricultural development most difficult.
Africa is certainly not a cursed continent, but nature seems to be
more demanding and puts more complex obstacles in the way of
human evolution.

There is no society without a culture of its own. Every social organization presupposes a common effort and a common response to its environment, and therefore it demands common obligations. Basically, culture is the totality of accepted options on how to live, act, think, and dominate a given physical and historical situation. Man is never entirely free—his conscience, his scruples, or his satisfactions and his pleasures express his cultural conditioning. Our personalities owe little to genetics and much to the cultural environment of our childhood. Psychologists underline the importance of mother and father images—the mother and the father are first and foremost representatives of our society and cultural environment.

To a certain degree, the traditional African environment admits the individual's liberty in adapting and interpreting novel cultural values. One has the right to demand flexibility in understanding them, but at one's own peril. The cultural environment has deep roots and is incapable of radical change and immediate response.

Ours is a reversed kind of cultural ignorance. For instance, "music" to us means Gregorian chant, counterpoint, Mozart, or Schoenberg. If we say "theater" we subconsciously identify the concept with dramatic representations from Aeschylus to Shakespeare to Anouilh and Arthur Miller. Very few among us will naturally consider Asian and African music, dance, or theater as equally relevant, expressive, and meaningful. We forget that ours is only one of many cultures, and that its values do not necessarily correlate with others. Differences are by no means misunderstandings. Opposition and resentment are generated if and when a cultural environment has to defend its fundamental belief in its own finality.

Even the idea of different rationalities, different concepts of logic, are difficult to us. Ours is a world of struggle and conquests between men and nature. There is hardly a moment's respite in our quest for material betterment in our mental efforts to enlarge our frontiers into the unknown. Adam and Eve are driven from Paradise; Jacob fights the Angel; Prometheus steals the fire of the gods. Our very spirit is forever critical, searching, and adventurous, never satisfied with the present, always longing for an unattainable future.

Man, in Africa, could not fight hostile nature but had to accept its powerful domination. He *had* to accommodate himself to nature's slow rhythm. The local gods and spirits in the pantheon of most African mythologies are naturebound and hostile to humanity. They have to be pacified by a complicated ritual of adoration and service, and at the same time their innate animosity has to be overcome by ruse and deception.

Ancestor worship appeases the hostile forces of nature. The worshipped ancestor image symbolizes and deifies not only the continuing power and influence of the dead, but also sanctifies the jealously guarded social customs and beliefs. The godly ancestor will direct his human offspring and intercede in their behalf if they consent to obey unquestioningly the community's social and religious taboos. But each individual transgression will cause the punishment of the group.

Spirits of nature—divinities like Mother Earth, the Sun God, and Thunder God—and godly ancestors exist side by side in chaotic profusion. There is no clear interconnection, no hierarchy among the powers—only competition and strife. Man is the defenseless target of the gods. He must strive to live, giving the least offense possible. He must continually mobilize other strong spirits and divine forces to plead his case with the easily offended divinities. Hunting, for example, becomes a complicated ritual of appeasement of the Forest Gods, the safekeepers of beasts. Masks disguise the hunters' identities, sacrifices are offered, the hunters often go through a ceremony of purification before returning to the village. The celebratory feast is not only one of Thanksgiving but one in which the people ask forgiveness for having mastered nature. In the case of an unsuccessful hunt or an unforeseen calamity of some sort, as for instance, the accidental death of a hunter, it is said that the Forest God has proved his strength and must be appeased by sacrifice and ritual. Mother Earth, the goddess of fertility and soil, may react in much the same way as the Forest God. Rivers, trees, mountains, and lakes are the abode of independent spirits who must be appeased and worshiped. Without neutralizing their animosity or obtaining their consent, man has little chance of survival in the all-hostile environment. So a driving force in an African's existence is the effort to obtain control over supernatural powers for himself and his group. He therefore believes in the powers of talismans and amulets to provide good fortune and protection. In the face of disaster—sickness, barrenness, drought, or war—the African will turn for help to his ancestral spirits and to magic.

The animistic religions of Africa once severely controlled the use and practice of magic. Those who used it for their private or personal ends were often harshly punished. Only in times of great danger to society, in war or during epidemics, did magic play a more central part in the ritual. The adoration of the divinities—ancestors and natural spirits—was always central to animistic belief, and the use of magic marginal. Its widespread appearance today is a symptom of the disintegration of the old cultural environment and the present cultural void in large parts of African society.

Now, Magic is pervasive, as a key used to compel the occult forces of man and nature to action. Magic may be constructive or destructive, because its forces can be directed according to the intention of the individual user. Anthropologists have pointed out —as African leaders probably instinctively knew—that the need for magic tends to be strong in situations of social upheaval, and uncertainty in personal relations. So it is not surprising to find its main impact among the detribalized urban populations of the African cities. Islam and Christianity have prestige value as the religions of conquering civilizations, but the belief in magic is never far from the African social surface. Even among the educated urban elite ancestor worship and magic beliefs are quietly observed—outwardly at least, as a sign of piety and national solidarity.

The formation of a modern African economy is being obstructed by this common trust in magic, for it paralyzes economic ambition with the irrational fatalism it engenders. You have to live in Africa to grasp fully its all-encompassing and destructive influence.

An example may illustrate one aspect of the peculiar blend of magic and economics. The "multiplier" is a well-known West African "magician" type—seldom brought to trial: the man who will take a little sum of money from his victim and through magic "multiply" the amount four to six times, returning the profit to his client. The attraction is so great that the victim returns with larger and larger sums to be "multiplied" by magic. Invariably, the magic in the end does not work, and the largest sum is spirited away by a spell of "bad magic." (In one capital city on the West Coast, one of these "multipliers" was brought to trial. He was a near-illiterate, pious old man whose properties included three modern apartment buildings and other real estate estimated at seven hundred thousand dollars. The prosecution had great difficulties in obtaining witnesses. The sentence was light.)

Other, more serious examples abound. The farmer believes that once his field is sown, the harvest is in the hands of the gods and spirits. Old and trusted employees leave their job overnight because they are convinced their life is threatened by witchcraft. Two or three slight accidents in a factory give rise to the belief that a bad spell has been cast. Some African presidents and ministers will not leave the capital on certain weekdays, and others will not use an airplane for travel abroad. It is well known that marabouts, animistic priests, and witch doctors have been invited to the highest councils of the governments.

The African's animistic beliefs are strongly related to tribal customs, rituals, and ancestral rules. To abandon even one feature could mean the collapse of his spiritual—not to say physical—universe. He is afraid to cut himself off from family and community. And he rightly hesitates to look to Western civilization and its values for the answers to his needs and quests.

But we—we modern Westerners—are powerless to neutralize the

destructive mischief and irrational behavior created by the belief in magic and superstition. And, as yet, the African elite has not actively opposed this social disease. The profiteers of popular superstitions—the marabouts, exorcisers, and witch doctors—are often recognized and honored personalities. The leaders cooperate with them out of political expediency—and a carefully cultivated attachment to archaic popular superstitions and belief in the potency of magic. The African elite, in and outside government, must take the side of enlightenment and fight the nefarious effects of popular mystifications.

This is the price of progress!

JANUARY 25

African cultures have shown an astonishing degree of vitality and resistance to Western influences. The Africans brought in slavery to the Caribbean and Brazil hundreds of years ago still cling to their old beliefs. Despite becoming Christian generations ago, the Brazilian Makumba ritual is still African in form and content. Even the songs and prayers are still recited in Yoruba and Abomey. Here or there some Christian saint is borrowed to camouflage the old African deity. The belief in the forces of magic is still powerful and has influenced non-Negro sections of the population.

JANUARY 26

The demands and aspiration of the individual and the cultural flexibility of his environment are seldom compatible. Every time a given culture is confronted with new or unknown influences affecting its stability or questioning its wisdom, there will appear the strong resistance of conservatism. The environment will respond in self-defense. Examples are easy. Food, for instance, is far from being simply a matter of nutrition to be absorbed for the body's upkeep. It has inherent irrational qualities. Westerners eat frogs' legs and shrimps, but are disgusted with Africans eating grasshoppers or monkey meat. We don't seem to understand how difficult it is for an entire society to adopt *our* eating habits, even if the only alternative is famine. The refusal to eat unknown food is symbolic of an entire sociocultural environment's repudiation of the strange and foreign.

Why should we have expected that the closed traditional societies of Africa would assimilate new values more easily than the interconnected and open societies of the West? Two years ago we shipped 300 tons of selected sorghum seeds to the drought-stricken Northeast. To our great surprise we found little enthusiasm for our gift—in a population stricken by famine. The farmers accepted the gift but consumed most of it, rather reluctantly, or tried to exchange it for the bad local seeds. Nothing we did could change this. Later we found out that their local seeds were tiny and reddish—ours were large and white. The differences in color and taste accounted for their reticence and opposition.

As always in cases of this kind, there was no organized vocal opposition. Neither a chief nor a marabout tried to influence the farmers. The people reacted through an invisible, subconscious consensus. There were a few exceptions—mostly in the form of a peculiar compromise according to which some young farmers made reluctant use of our variety of seeds in the dry, higher fields while they used the old seeds for the best, low, well-irrigated lands. The ghastly results were apparent from the start. This project was in the hands of the African government's agricultural services. I have no doubt that the young African technicians did their best to explain, flatter, and even pressure the farmers to use the new seeds. But, without voicing dissent or doubt, I gained the impression, later confirmed by both Africans and Europeans, that the farmers were unable to express any rationale for their objections: They simply did not accept the novelty.

Each ton of that seed-grain cost my government $550 in purchase, shipping, and trucking expenditures. If we had bought *African* sorghum or millet, with the same money we could have distributed eight times more grain—without encountering any resistance and without having to face recurrent failure. And we certainly did fail. We did not solve the seed problem nor did we substantially improve the food situation in the drought area. And we spent $160,000 instead of $20,000. The crucial dilemma remains: "Could we have prevented this costly fiasco?"

JANUARY 27

Caste and social status—another facet. A typical ranking system in West Africa once ran approximately like this: (1) chiefs and nobles; (2) freemen (warriors); (3) artisans; (4) freed slaves; (5) griots; and (6) slaves. Each caste had its own privileges and responsibilities, its own rituals, its own sphere of social and economic obligations. The caste was originally an entirely closed group, and even today there is very limited social mobility among castes. Intermarriages are still rare and are considered transgressions. The caste system cannot be fitted into Western patterns of economics or governmental authority, which are based on education, personal ambition and ability, free opportunity and technical knowledge.

African governments seldom fight the excesses of the caste structures openly: they try to compromise. A cabinet minister from a lower caste will try to surround himself with councillors of an old and aristocratic lineage. A departmental head will treat his illiterate office boy very deferentially if he is a scion of a higher-class family. A well-known left-wing head of state rewrote his family tree in order to make himself more respectable in the eyes of the majority of his people. Some of Africa's most outstanding personalities have little chance to reach high positions in government because of their low caste. With few exceptions, the heads of state are nobles. Some are actually the dynastic rulers of one of their nation's large ethnic units.

So the old exists together with the new. The caste system, with its concepts of inherited status and authority, is still all powerful in the countryside. Western social concepts are prevalent in the cities and are applied in the Europeanized sectors of the economy and within the government administration. The contradiction between the two systems paralyzes African chances for development.

The gradual emancipation of women is directly related to the caste and status problem. It is yet another issue making for social conflict. Contrary to some Western impressions, African women occupy a central and honored position in tribal society. Except in some exceptionally pious Islamic states in north and central Africa, the role of the woman is strong and independent. The woman cultivates the fields, prepares the food with all its ritual significance, and is responsible for the manifold fertility rites. She settles marriage questions and their material obligations. She has the right to divorce and return to her own family group. She has important religious and ritual responsibilities and has great influence on the education of the young. She is often economically independent of her husband, and in matrilineal societies she may reach the position of a chief or ruler of her people. Her position is honored and secure in tribal law and custom.

An African woman moving from the village into the city is left without a hearth, without the ritual festivities, and without her own fields. She will feel deprived of her most cherished position—her status. She will instinctively accuse the city of being responsible for her plight, and she will oppose forcefully its new social and cultural patterns. Only in education and the possibility of her finding a professional career will her resistance be overcome.

Only a few African women have achieved either a full education or a modern career. The vast majority, about 90 per cent, are still illiterate, and little is done to explain the part women must play in the process of modernization—or to prepare them for it.

Here again, much can be done with Western assistance, but the impetus must come from the African elite itself. Until now, it has shown little understanding. The minute educated and professional female elite struggles against considerable discrimination.

Today's African ruling class is composed mostly of gifted higher-caste sons who have enjoyed the freedom of many student years abroad. On their return to Africa, they find themselves obliged to marry women in their ethnic and caste groups. Frequently these girls come from the country: they are often half-literate and generally entirely unprepared for the society in which their husbands feel at home. Very seldom do the wives of high government officials accompany their husbands to social functions and rarely are they capable of partaking in their social and intellectual lives. This situation has traumatic effects on the family unit, especially on the mother-child relationship. Some years ago, I helped to bring a group of "very important" married women to my country for a three-month seminar on the subject "How to conduct a modern home and social life." The results were astonishing. In no more than three months' time, the women learned to express themselves and gained a self-assurance in public they had never felt before. Not only the women, but especially their husbands, were deeply grateful.

JANUARY 29

In Western civilization, work is not only the main condition of progress but a positive moral imperative. For years, missionaries and European technicians in Africa have preached the beauty and dignity of labor. But tribal life is leisurely—there is always time for a rest, a feast, a palaver under the village tree. The rural African walks slowly: he does not hurry. He is not pursued by notions of lost time or time-is-money. To him, work is a painful but necessary burden. It is done preferably in large village groups accompanied by song and the rhythmic sound of a tam-tam. One labors to feed one's family and group, to amass the bride-price, and to gain some status. But work has no moral connotations.

Money, as such, is new to Africa. A subsistence economy has only a barter market, in which foods, simple goods and products, and domesticated animals are exchanged. As family groups produce more or less the same products, regional market transactions are limited. Very early, the excess production in this barter system brought forth an "economy of ostentation." African cattle and foodstocks were, and are still, amassed for neither their commercial nor nutritive value. Instead, the owner's rank and status is determined by the number of heads he owns. It does not matter that his herds are unproductive: he does not think in terms of the financial value of his ownership. If he needs food or cloth he will sell or exchange an animal, but he regrets this transaction as a loss of capital. The bride-price, the festivities, the funeral celebrations—all will be paid for by cattle or foodstocks.

Certainly Africa has moved with impressive speed into the money economy during the last fifty years. Indeed, Africans have shown an amazing commercial ingenuity. But the psychological transition from the village subsistence economy to a modern money economy will take time. Meanwhile, the saving of money, banking transactions, and the commercial use of credits and loans are exceptions to the rule.

I remember that in 1966, an international agency wanted urgently to purchase grain in West Africa for relief purposes—that is, to buy excess African harvests instead of importing expensive Western foods. The African and European technicians found, to their surprise, that the stock bins were overflowing with decayed corn—it had been there for years and was badly damaged by worms and insects—totally unfit for consumption. Even then, the farmers were reluctant to sell. The corn was the symbol of their social status.

FEBRUARY 2

The notion of economic and social *development* was conceived and conditioned in the West. Science, research, industrial capacity, and financial power are the cornerstones of our society. But the African asks himself if all that is really as progressive and worth-while as we would have him believe. He has participated in two world wars, and he has seen the drabness of our industrial suburbs, the alienation of so many of our people, and, above all, the great loneliness and sadness of modern man.

An African farmer to whom the use of chemical fertilizers was explained, rested from his work. He had a doubtful air. "I am content," he said pensively. "My family has enough to eat, and we have enough clothes to wear—one for work and one for the feast days. We celebrate our festivities and invite family and friends, and they, in turn, invite us. . . . I am content." He wanted us to understand that his doubts were not caused by the fertilizer itself, but he feared that the novelty would break the delicate balance in his economic and social condition and would carry him into unknown spheres of affluence. If the fertilizer did not increase his income considerably, he might be in debt. If it did, his neighbors might become envious and his family group would demand more and more from him. His wives would ask for new amenities and his sons might not want to stay in the village. His judgment expressed the life experience and wisdom of his culture. African proverbs and fables compliment the wise man who prefers stability to change and human contentment to strife and ambition.

But in terms of historic reality, our farmer has no choice. European civilization penetrated Africa centuries ago. Western values in education, government, and economy are here to stay and affect even larger sectors of the African population. The burning question remains: Can Africa absorb and assimilate these new values and "Africanize" the new techniques demanded by the modern age? Or will the Old Africa oppose and castigate these modern values indiscriminately, gradually lose its vitality, and push the farmer and the others into the despair of a cultural void?

FEBRUARY 3

There are no protected islands in our world. A nation's possession of technological know-how, its basic industrial capacity, is closely linked to its political power and standing. Poor nations are dependent nations, open to humiliation and censure.

The political and intellectual elites of Africa accept with fervor modern norms and values. But they are well aware that a majority of their population is ambivalent about or opposed to change. Here are the root causes of the political and cultural imbalances peculiar to all underdeveloped nations. The pressures of a stagnant economy, together with the centrifugal forces released by cultural mutations, require the elite to formulate a long-term policy of national development—a major political decision. But opinions divide and attitudes clash over two diametrically opposed philosophies. African leadership is wrestling with a choice between two concepts of development: evolution or revolution.

Development cannot be measured by economic progress alone, say the evolutionists. Development is a human condition that expresses itself primarily as a social movement. Economic problems can only be solved successfully in coordination with the absorptive capacity of the African people. Modernization cannot be imposed from outside. New systems of production, new machinery, and a new mode of life are of use only if they can be introduced without opposing the cultural environment, by responding to its changing needs.

The revolutionists disagree at this point. An evolutionary process is necessarily slow; the selective choice of development targets, their adaptation to the environment, and the continuous dialogue with the social group involved is a long, problematic process. The revolutionists prefer the strong-arm method: the imposition of a Western educational system, the enforcement of a new discipline in labor relations, the enforced implementation of an agricultural policy aimed at establishing large-scale tropical plantations whose products can be sold on the world market, and the gradual but enforced elimination of the old power structure of chiefs, elders, and marabouts.

The advocates of the tough line believe that the old traditional society has to be exploded from within. Its disappearance is a prerequisite for development and modernization. Examples and parallels from nineteenth-century Europe are quoted extensively. The proletarization of the rural population and its movement into the cities is to be encouraged; political and social agitation and consciousness will then supersede tribal affinities and divisions. Only then will Africa be ready to enter the modern age.

This revolutionary approach has its temptations. It is simple, clear, and sufficiently dogmatic to please Western minds. But its faults lie precisely in this simplicity.

The historical comparison with nineteenth-century Europe does not seem convincing to me. The situations are not comparable. The human motivations are different. Africa has to overcome a colonial heritage which left deep scars upon her collective personality. Africans obtained political independence in a condition of doubt and frustration about their own capacity to create a meaningful national existence. Even the most liberal colonial system had smothered the social, cultural, and political initiatives of the colonized—either by force or by acculturation, mostly by both.

For many generations the colonized accepted this unequal situation, but with the gradual formation of an African intelligentsia, reaction and intellectual awareness set in, finding its expression in the quest for national independence. This goal achieved, the African intellectual has found himself more dependent than ever upon his former masters. His economy is still part of the former colonial empire. He is assisted financially and technically by the former metropolis. The cultural frustration is even more painful and destructive. With each step he takes to modernization, he has to contest the cultural values of his own background. This he is reluctant to do—not because he is incapable of using force, but because he has not evolved an *African* alternative to the old order. Therefore he hesitates. But hesitation is no surrogate for a policy.

FEBRUARY 7

Most of the African elite is, as yet, undecided and leaderless. Extremists—whether from the right or left—have no great personal or ideological appeal: African leaders are educated in the liberal European tradition, based upon the rationality of a coherent cultural environment. But they are at a loss to understand why certain European techniques are easily adaptable to Africa while others fail. Many of those techniques have a positive social significance and are successful wherever they are applied. The use of antibiotics and vaccines, the building of bridges, and roads are generally accepted and even welcomed by the mass of the African people. But the moment new developments touch the *social fabric* of African society, complications arise. At that point, the African political leadership is not ready for a confrontation but will compromise or retreat.

Especially in a one-party state, political power is still centered in the rural areas. No government administration can disregard the reaction or mood of an important rural region. For this reason, African governments act on two separate levels: they invite and demand international or bilateral aid and cooperate diligently with their Western partners at the initial planning stages. But they will be careful to leave the implementation of the projects in the hands of Europeans. If and when a technique or project is accepted and integrated into the social fabric, the European technicians will be replaced by local personnel. If, as it often happens, the rural population oppose or reject a project, then they will blame the fiasco on the West's deficient planning, lack of manpower or investment, or miscomprehension of local conditions. They will point out that even though the project failed, the region gained something in the value of the buildings, roads, irrigation equipment, or machinery invested. With their Western partners, they will take a different attitude altogether, and demand that the experiment continue: more money, more manpower, more time, more modifications.

It is hard to know whether the African administrations are conscious of this duality or whether it is a conditioned, self-defensive reflex. But they lose on both levels. Their Western partners are frustrated, and on the African level they lose prestige and standing.

There can be no doubt: African administrations are the natural channels through which flow the new ideas and initiatives. Yet once you leave the limits of the capital cities, governments are distrusted and feared, but seldom respected, being regarded as a kind of foreign authority. African leaders have to be very careful indeed not to aggravate the tensions within the rural environment. Underground oppositions to their regime take easy advantage, either in the cities or in the interior. The cities can be controlled by the army and police, but the countryside, sheltering 80–90 per cent of the population, has to be cajoled and won over. The use of force could be tantamount to a political failure of national magnitude. The government acts as if the long-term objective of modernization can be imposed on the rural population by a peculiar indirect tactic of palaver and immediate economic advantages, taking care not to touch on the deeper economic and cultural implications. Needless to say, this approach is seldom successful—often self-defeating.

That reminds me of a telling incident. Years ago, a good African friend in the government wanted to see me on an important personal matter. "Please do take my sister's oldest son, a five-year-old, for medical treatment to your country. He is ill, and we cannot treat him here. The boy has symptoms of leprosy." I explained to my friend that his own country was much better equipped to deal with leprosy than my own, simply because of the rarity of the disease there. "But you don't understand," my nervous visitor argued. "We cannot treat the boy here. It would destroy his family socially and would affect even my standing. Leprosy is known to affect only the lowest classes of our society. If it hits a family like ours, it is not any more the question of an illness—it is a social calamity. This is not a question of money: only help me to get the boy quietly into a European institution where he can stay until he is cured."

So, in the face of its dilemma—on one side the Western partner demanding immediate modernization, on the other the counter-pressures of a malcontent population—the elite has evolved neither an ideology nor personal convictions of its own. It manages but does not lead. Yet without a personal conviction of the justice and absolute necessity of constructing a modern Africa on new values, it can have no consistent policy, no constructive opposition to the archaism of the past.

Away from home, the same elite will show great revolutionary drive and fervor. On the international scene, they will unhesitatingly adopt the most adventurous postures. But progressiveness and revolutionary attitudes should start at home. Otherwise, they are empty of significance, devoid of content—an extravagance which nobody takes seriously. The African elite has yet to show the responsible stamina of true leadership.

The West has approached the problem of Africa's modernization with a mixture of straightforward technical skill and a patronizing attitude of a donor "who knows best because he holds
the purse strings." The problems generated by Africa's cultural
mutation are not officially recognized as relevant questions. By
Western standards, the African government is sovereignly responsible for its internal affairs; would it not be improper even to question its aptitude in dealing with these problems?

Behind this veil of propriety, the Western partners accept "only
technical and financial responsibility" for the many assistance
schemes in Africa. But in reality, this working arrangement has
proven inadequate and illusory. Western public opinion has become pessimistic. Aid budgets are delayed and trimmed. More and
more of the Western aid capacity is channeled into costly "parade"
projects: hotels, office buildings, stadiums, theaters, and televi-
sion stations, which, once established, burden the government
with suffocating maintenance budgets. This shortsighted approach
seems to serve the short-term interests of both partners best. The parade project has an inherent political propaganda value to the Western donor. Its imposing modern symbolism responds to the local
government's urge for ostentatious and speedy Westernization.
But the parade project only deepens the gap, because it does not
respond to African needs. It is a kind of stage setting, supposedly
necessary to modern statehood. Economically, it is useless. And by
its very nature it is parasitical, requiring the employment of European technicians and a huge maintenance budget.

Yet the surface Westernization of African cities progresses
quickly. Unemployment has reached flood levels. Slums abound.
The migration into the cities continues. An alienated, permanently unemployed sub-proletariat constitutes one of the most
explosive social and political factors on the scene.

There is no doubt: Western aid and assistance is retreating into
the marginal realms of Africa's struggle for progress. The West
has failed to inspire a self-perpetuating movement affecting the

root causes of African underdevelopment. The crisis of the West's system of cooperation with Africa is now acute. All our old attitudes and approaches are being questioned. We have reached a critical stage. What is to be done?

Today, during one of my farewell visits, I had an animated two-hour conversation with the youngest minister in the cabinet. What an outspoken, intelligent, and bitter man! It all started with a joke: if the U.S. and the U.S.S.R. would have executed their space research with the same budgets and efficiency as they invested in African development, he said, the first men would arrive on the moon in the year 3000. I answered that the great attraction of the moon is that it is uninhabitable, and there would be no need for its development.

He took my repartee more seriously than necessary, and attacked the whole array of Western attitudes, intentions, and policies in Africa: the world cannot continue with the division between the many poor and the few rich nations poisoning international relations. The rich nations, in enlightened self-interest, should make a special effort to help the developing nations. Otherwise, the poor nations will be drawn into a cycle of revolutionary confrontations with the rich.

But that argument is shaky on two accounts, and I told him so. Poor and rich nations have always existed, and poverty and underdevelopment are hardly novel historical occurrences. The causes of revolution or civil war are internal, motivated by social or national tensions, and they are liable to occur even in rich societies. International aid given by rich to poor nations is a new historical concept, proven very successful in postwar Europe, but running into unexpected difficulties in Africa two decades later.

The Minister disagreed. In his opinion, the industrialized countries owe their wealth and prosperity to their past and present colonial exploitation of the poor nations. It would be only just and decent to return part of the loot. Furthermore, the industrialized nations need to sell their finished products to the "proletarian states." So it is in their best interests to raise the purchasing power of the poor nations through increased development.

But instead, he continued, the rich nations' attitude has a large element of patronizing contempt. He mentioned the UNCTAD conference in New Delhi in 1968 as a pertinent example—where, he argued, the West demonstrated its desire to keep the underdeveloped nations forever poor and dependent. He gave me some illustrations: the hospitals, schools, and stadiums built in Africa with Western aid are arranged so that only 20 per cent of the investment is spent in the country, while 80 per cent returns to the donor in payments for building materials, machinery, or salaries. Instead of respecting a five-year development plan as a self-contained entity, the donor countries pick out projects suited better for themselves than for the recipient. In all these matters, the West has proven its unwillingness and incapacity to cooperate. The poor nations will thus have no choice but to force the rich nations by political and economic pressures into a position in which sufficient aid will be given as a matter of course and not as charity.

At the beginning, I was rather taken aback by his unexpected frankness. But I decided to take the bull by the horns. After all, his ideas deserved clear answers. "Your Excellency," I replied, "if you really have found the means to force the rich nations into greater cooperation then I would not waste a moment in employing them. But I am afraid you will not succeed. The New Delhi conference proved that the many poor and weak cannot force the powerful few into negotiations on their own terms. Economic capacity and political power are closely related. You can't change facts. A bridge built in Africa is one bridge less somewhere else, because even Western wealth is limited. Let me mention one figure: the poor nations, four-fifths of mankind, participate in only 20 per cent of world trade and, if we deduct the Middle Eastern oil, only 12 per cent. So the rich nations trade among themselves. They could continue to develop at the same rate without the oil and without the economic participation of the poor nations. The tragedy is that you refuse to face these facts, while the rich, realizing the situation, gradually disengage themselves. In this field there is no great difference between the basic attitudes of the U.S. and the Soviet Union, only one of nuance—although the West has extended twenty times more aid and assistance than the Communist countries during the last ten years. Only in arms shipments are both blocs equal.

"I agree that the Western world is unjust, full of contradictions and pettiness—ambiguous attitudes that are simultaneously cynical and naïve. But you *must* understand these contradictions! For instance, the notion of international assistance for development is an original, and even generous, idea. It was invented and applied first by the Americans to rebuild war-ravaged Europe twenty years ago. For $10 billion over a period of ten years, the United States saved Europe from the economic and political disintegration we witnessed after World War I. The Marshall Plan was economically successful, but it was a political failure. Never were Americans more disliked and attacked than during the years they helped most. Men and nations resent being objects of philanthropy.

"When those ideas and experiences were applied to the newly independent African and Asian nations, something went wrong. The sickness did not respond to the medication. Still, the fact remains that every year the new nations receive almost the financial equivalent of the entire Marshall Plan investment—$10 billion. But where are the results?

"The point is, the West approached the problem here mainly from an economic and technological angle—the aspect it understands best—and failed bitterly. Now, ten years and $100 billion later, we confront not a simple technical miscalculation, but an abysmal misunderstanding. The West was and is unable to see development as a cultural mutation and a socio-political movement. The Western conception is mathematical. This is its major fault. Two and two do not make four if you live in a tribal subsistence economy. Of course, it is easy to criticize others. But aren't the African governments as responsible for the failures as the donors? Haven't you committed sins of omission? Instead of guiding and inspiring the development effort in key areas like agriculture, basic industry, health, and technical education, you created a top-heavy, costly bureaucracy incapable of productive action. You even created an ideology that defines assistance and aid as something the world owes you. But development means modernization on all levels. There is no economic modernization without modernizing the cultural values and the social structures of African society. But political leadership has to lead, educate, and convince—with endless patience."

Here the Minister cut into my long monologue. "Mr. Ambassador, are you not overdramatizing the situation? Our GNP and per capita incomes are moving ahead—slowly, perhaps, but definitely forward. We have tripled our educational facilities. We have started industrial ventures of economic importance. Our population is better educated and fed than ever before. Our government may not be efficient, but it governs neither better nor worse than others. Without wanting to antagonize—I ask only out of curiosity—how did it happen that the development projects you undertook did not entirely succeed?"

"Your Excellency," I retorted. "Your rate of progress is sufficient to disturb and crack the old order, to effect social turbulence, migration into the cities, and unemployment, but insufficient to solve the problems it created. There, precisely, lies the danger. As long as the GNP and per capita income are not doubled, as long as you do not reach the take-off point, Africa is in danger of staying underdeveloped for generations.

"Your second question is difficult to answer. At the beginning, my critical faculties were drowned by the enormity of Africa's needs and by my government's financial and technical willingness to be of assistance. Later, the difficulties started a process of inquiry and stocktaking. I certainly haven't changed my mind about the imperative necessity of increased Western aid to Africa, but its system and method of application must change. Let me explain:

"Today, I would not plan a poultry project on technical and economic data alone, but would insist on a detailed socio-psychological report on the urban and rural populations' attitudes, and dispositions to integrate our project into the fabric of their lives.

If I found out that 75 per cent of the people refuse to consume eggs, I would change our plans. For instance, I would request your government to invest a part of our aid budget in an educational campaign promoting eggs! In other words, I would suggest that educational campaigns, of long duration, run simultaneously and in cooperation with physical projects."

The Minister looked doubtful. An educational campaign would take years to affect a change and possibly create more tension and animosity than understanding. Anyhow, more than two hundred assistance projects were at this moment in progress. "Do you seriously propose to launch educational campaigns for each and every project?" I gave the obvious answer: "Only when the project touches the cultural fabric of the population."

"At this point, let me ask you a question to which I never received a convincing answer. Your administration is composed of trained and dedicated technicians who know local conditions well. Why was I not told four years ago, when we launched the poultry project, that we might encounter widespread public reticence and superstitions? Why did you keep that secret? Why didn't one of your technicians, who knew the plans by heart, explain that our concrete-block houses for the settlement project were unacceptable to the farmers? Someone must have known that. Why were we kept in the dark?"

The Minister looked at me pensively. "Sir, your straightforward questions invite clear answers. You know that development projects are one of our most important sources of national income. This year, our intake from foreign aid almost equals our national budget. We try our utmost to attract development projects to our country—this is our interest and duty. But I am convinced, Mr. Ambassador, nobody wanted to mislead you. If you had asked your questions at the time, we would have answered them as well as we could. You did not ask them because you were unaware of their importance. Well, you may ask, why didn't we volunteer the information? As I said, we are interested in attracting development projects—not in making ,it difficult to implement them. We know by experience that our Western partners avoid projects that

create social or cultural antagonism or political tensions. This
would be counterproductive to their interests. So we are naturally
careful not to inflate these matters.

"There's another thing. I am from the South and I could have
told you, more or less, how the sixteen villages in my region would
react to your settlement scheme. However, I do not know how a
nearby region would have responded. Even in my own district my
predictions might have been wrong, because I do not live there
anymore. Let me be frank. My government's main task is economic development. Large segments of our population are opposed
to change and therefore opposed to the government. You have an
advantage we do not possess: you are foreign, rich, feared, and
command powerful force in the form of airplanes, fertilizers, and
tractors, etc. Our people will not directly oppose you but will try to
discover if they, too, can master some of your White Magic. If
they finally decide to reject an experiment like your settlement
scheme, they will be sorry to disappoint you and explain that what
is good for the White Man is not always good for us.

"As you well know, we often employ European technicians on
our own projects, simply because they have a much better chance
to get things done with our rural population. So we are resented
by a majority of our own people for modernizing too fast, and
we antagonize our Western friends for not modernizing fast
enough. . . . African administrations have to take all these frustrations in their stride."

"My friend," I cut in. "You and I agree that the actual method
of development is outdated and in need of review and reappraisal.
I am sure that these impressions are common to many. We are
afraid that our common development effort is in danger of being
drowned by the sheer weight of its contradictions and failures.
Let us start somewhere. I confess that, recently, I began to
put on paper my experiences and my opinions on problems of
African development—the attempt of an observer and a friend to
come to terms with the complex motive forces of Africa today. I
hope to stress Africa's very special cultural environment, because
its elusiveness made our pragmatic approach so questionable in

the past. I want to analyze why our performance was erratic—but only to draw general conclusions for future action. Nothing is further from my mind than another detailed plan for the reorganization of international cooperation—others have done that! But perhaps my reflections and records will encourage a change in attitude, injecting new vitality into this fateful venture."

The Minister laughed, and wished me many interesting hours with my writing. We parted good friends.

I am working hard to put my notes in order. The number of topics I want to deal with grows by the hour, and my papers are assuming flood-like proportions. My friend will have to wait.

I'm beginning to feel like the sorcerer's apprentice.

The Ambassador's Economic Report

THE PRECEDING OBSERVATIONS OF THE AMBASSADOR are his personal notes, but a reader might also like to see one of his official economic reports which he so labored over and despaired of translating into human terms. As he once wrote to a friend, "Belles lettres and economics are incompatible!"

The Ambassador usually prefaced his reports with a personal letter to soften their "rigidity."

December 22, 196–

Dear John:

Who knows better than you that "economese" is as dull and boring to me as Mozart to the deaf; but our Minister of Finance—do you remember how we used to call him the Wizard?—has succeeded in putting all of us in Africa into an ambiguous and, I think, untenable position with that one speech opening the general debate on the new budget. Please remember my cable of 7 April (A/EC/1602) about my talk with the Foreign Minister here on this subject. It goes without saying that his remarks are regarded as a danger signal, a prelude to the additional retraction of our financial and technical-aid commitment to Africa, marking a major change in our attitude toward the whole structure of financial and technical assistance which we helped to build.

You will remember that our Minister gave two main reasons for the impending cut in the foreign-aid budget for the new nations: (1) the sudden difficulties experienced in our own economy—the unexpectedly negative balance of payments creating unusual financial stress, the way our economy was overheating and was therefore experiencing inflationary pressures with resultant unemployment, a setback in government spending, etc.; (2) our African partners' shortcomings, which, in our Minister's schoolmasterish opinion, are "serious obstacles." He referred to African administrations' being inefficient in taking over development schemes prepared, staffed, and financed for them by us; to the current political instability, social unrest, and even internal warfare; and (here he was true to form) to the shortcomings of African governments—their status budgets for prestige functions, air-conditioned limousines, theaters, stadiums, swanky official residences (all unnecessary in his opinion). He also questioned the economic wisdom of spending millions on intra-African or international festivals, conferences, and state visits and thundered against officialdom's high standard of living as compared with the subsistence level of a miserable population.

So, in all, he said, our financial and technical-assistance program, instead of creating the desired snowballing effect throughout the African economy, was spotty, without national impact anywhere, mostly unprofitable and, therefore, an economic liability. His concluding remarks, sweetening the pill, were most equivocal: He spoke of an increase in our contributions to the international agencies involved in African development, but in his wisdom, he did not mention the amount, nor did he explain why multilateral aid would succeed where a bilateral effort had failed. The impression left upon my African clientele is that he simply tried to camouflage our retreat.

Let me concede: I have little doubt that the individual facts he mentioned were exact. But for a representative of a state with a $2,000 per capita annual income to preach piously to countries with a $100 per capita income—that needed the peculiar courage of self-righteousness. What do the facts prove? And why did he overlook, for instance, the fact that our defense budget is still some twenty-five times larger than the amount we allocate to foreign aid? Why did he have to make this offensive statement instead of simply doing what he had to do and keeping quiet about it? Did he have an eye on the conservative opposition? Or did he intend to assure our voters that the government will not condone additional taxation so long as there are other possible expenditures that can be cut down? Why was this statement historically so inexact and politically so inexpedient? Why was he bound to arrive at the wrong conclusions? This I believe I have proved in the economic report attached. (The figures are taken mostly from U.N. publications, and from the International Monetary Fund and the World Bank. The conclusions are mine.)

How are your wife and the two boys? Where do you intend to spend your summer holidays? I look forward to hearing from you.

                                                                    Yours,

TO: Director of Department for Economic Affairs
cc: Director of Department for African Affairs
        Ministry of Finance: African Desk
        Ministry of Commerce and Industry: African Desk
        Archives
From: Ambassador C.F.S.

        Recapitulation and General Remarks to the
        ANNUAL ECONOMIC REPORT (1967-68)

        A. African Agriculture and the Deterioration
            of the Terms of Exchange

  B. African Mining Industries
  C. Investment in Underdevelopment
  D. Economics and Ideologies
  E. The Semantics of Development
  F. Conclusions and Proposals

A. AFRICAN AGRICULTURE AND THE DETERIORATION OF THE TERMS OF EXCHANGE

The underdeveloped nations are caught in a multiple cycle of economic asphyxiation: (1) permanently declining world prices for exportable raw materials; (2) permanently rising world prices for the finished industrial products needed for economic development; and (3) the population explosion.

Analysis of these three factors will give us at least a tentative understanding of the scope of modern Africa's economic problems and related social difficulties.

Naturally, the economic picture for the new nations varies greatly between one country and another and between regions and continents. But a typical symptom of economic underdevelopment recurs: the permanent decline of world prices for its monocultural, usually tropical, commodities. Since 1955, prices for these products have fallen by approximately 45 per cent. The reasons for this decline are manifold and differ for each commodity. Cotton, for instance, must compete with various cheaper synthetic fibers and is losing markets. Peanuts (groundnuts) are losing their markets because the competitive value of peanut oil is receding before new competitors like soya, sunflower, and corn oils which are all grown intensively and more cheaply in more temperate climates. Coffee and cocoa have underpriced themselves through overproduction. African rubber is also gradually losing its markets to synthetics and to the cheaper Southeast Asian product.

The gradual but erratic introduction in Africa of modern agricultural technology—the accrued use of chemical fertilizers, irrigation, the use of some insecticides and pesticides—has resulted in much higher yields but has not brought about a better cash income for the farmer. The volume of agricultural production of

African primary commodities increases 6–7 per cent annually, but income from increased production rises in absolute money terms only by 1–2 per cent yearly, because of the decline in world tropical commodity prices. In a continent where at least 80 per cent of the population is still actively involved in agriculture, this trend poses a crucial problem.

The second cycle of economic suffocation concerns Africa's need to import from the developed countries a whole array of industrial products—in order to modernize her economic infrastructure, to intensify her agriculture, and to invest in her infant industries. World prices for industrial and finished products rose by approximately 50 per cent during the ten years 1957–67, and this only decreased the capacity of underdeveloped countries to pave (and pay) their own way to the modernization and diversification of agriculture and industry. The African farmer today has to double his sales in order to obtain the same barter value he had ten or twelve years ago.

The third cycle is the most serious, the most depressing, and the most fatal of all: the permanently increasing rate of population growth. Africa's yearly net growth rate in population is conservatively considered to be at least 2.5 per cent.

The three cycles together—falling world prices for tropical produce, mounting world prices for industrial and finished goods, and the exploding demographic curve—create a 2–3 per cent annual loss of income for Africa and precipitate the gradual and tragic pauperization of the continent.

B. AFRICAN MINING INDUSTRIES

The poorest states of Africa are the landlocked ones in the center of the continent—with an average yearly per capita income of $50–60—amongst the lowest in the world. Here or there, however, mineral resources have been discovered and are being exploited, and their generally meager revenue covers at least a part of the government expenditures: for instance, diamonds in Sierra Leone, the Central African Republic, Guinea, and both Congos; oil in

Gabon and Nigeria; copper in Congo (Kinshasa) and Zambia; uranium in Gabon and Niger; iron ore and manganese in Liberia, Gabon, and Mauritania; bauxite in Guinea, Ghana, and Liberia; and phosphates in Senegal and Togo-Dahomey.

With few exceptions, African mineral riches are exploited and then shipped in their raw state to the industrialized Northern Hemisphere. Therefore they do not carry accrued value. The mines are not yet focal points for future industrial centers. Africa's manganese and iron ore deposits, with a density of 60–70 per cent, are among the world's richest, its phosphate fields have a 70–80 per cent purity, but there is not yet one chemical or industrial fertilizer enterprise for a continent in dire need of modernizing its agriculture. Africa produces 80 per cent of the world's industrial diamonds and almost all of its diamond gems. They are neither cut nor polished there. Copper production is enormous, supplying 30–40 per cent of the world's market. Part of it is refined in Africa, but no industrial complex making use of the raw material has yet been erected.

The historical reason for this situation is not difficult to understand. It is the result of the old economic relationship—between the industrialized colonizer and the raw-material-producing colonized. But ten years after political independence has been granted to most of the continent, no changes of any basic economic consequence have occurred. The few modern mechanized extraction and mining operations are owned by foreign interests, are geared to foreign needs, and accumulate foreign profits; their African economic importance is strictly localized; their modernizing influence is restricted to their own operational needs. They are closed industrial islands in the surrounding subsistence-economy sea. They exist like some kind of relay station for a distant industrialized world, responding and reacting to foreign needs and interests; yet the African economies are in dire need of the modernizing effect and the inherent capital attraction exercised by a natural industrial potential based on easily accessible raw materials.

This economic situation has created a peculiar psychological effect. During the industrial revolution in Europe, the shock of the breakdown of old social, political, and cultural patterns was greatly eased by the newly found material abundance, by a rapid growth in the standard of living, by a new scientific rationality, and a national mystique. But in the underdeveloped African economies, the existing industrial centers and the mechanized plantations are associated with the idea of foreign economic exploitation of national resources, and they are looked upon as foreign intrusions. In the minds of the people, they are extraneous to the economic and social body of the nation. Consequently, aspects of modernization and mechanization are confounded with the problem of foreign penetration and exploitation—and they encounter an opaque and irrational popular rejection. Much of the popular resistance to and distaste for modernization in Africa derives from this popular error, which confounds modern means of production with obscure, all-powerful foreign interests. A majority of the African population, therefore, has adopted a passive attitude toward the problems of its economic future. The African feels himself manipulated by forces he does not fully understand, over which he has no control. He feels victimized by an unknown destiny; he is resigned to this situation and expects to be helped and assisted; but his conscience is troubled.

C. *INVESTMENT IN UNDERDEVELOPMENT*

The most crucial problem facing the developing world is undoubtedly the lack of investment capital. Traditionally, investment capital has derived from two sources: national savings, or foreign investments in the form of loans or grants. Now, a nation must reinvest some 9 per cent of its gross national product to keep pace with an annual 2.5 per cent increase in population. But to modernize agricultural production and promote industrial capacity on top of that, it will have to invest 12–15 per cent of its GNP year after year to reach the "take-off" point toward self-sustained growth.

In Africa, the level of savings is necessarily low, composed mainly of so-called "forced" savings entering the national treasuries in the form of direct or indirect taxation. These savings do not amount to more than 5–7 per cent of the gross national income and, therefore, their productive potential is severely restricted, leaving the question of securing capital for economic development unresolved.

Foreign investment capital has been forthcoming through two main channels: the International Development Association and the World Bank. The IDA, which was established to lend money to emerging nations at low interest rates and on long terms, is virtually bankrupt because of political differences among its rich Western constituents. The World Bank, by demanding an interest rate of 6½ per cent, has put itself virtually out of reach of the poorer new nations. Still, more than $4 billion a year is repaid in interest rates and capital refunds by underdeveloped nations to the rich nations of the West—almost half of the annual capital flow of approximately $10 billion.

In the field of direct financial aid, the picture is even grimmer. The rich, industrialized nations, with an annual 4–5 per cent growth in GNP, spent at the beginning of the 1960's 0.9 per cent of their combined GNP on financial aid and technical assistance to underdeveloped countries; in 1967, they made available only 0.6 per cent. As a proportion of their GNP, then, the flow of investment capital, financial aid, and technical assistance was reduced by approximately 30 per cent during those seven years. It seems clear that military and other budgetary exigencies are forcing the major Western powers to make still deeper cuts in their minimal aid budgets. At the same time, it should be remembered, the wealthy nations, capitalist and Communist alike, are spending approximately $150 billion on military establishments and only $10 billion on capital and other economic aid to emerging nations. And not only the quantity of aid but the quality, i.e., its terms and conditions, is insufficient, entirely inadequate to meet the underdeveloped nations' urgent economic needs.

The role of private financial investment in Africa is difficult to ascertain. It is generally accepted that during the colonial period the flow of private capital amounted to more than half of all financial investments in Africa. The motives for this movement were simple—political stability, a monopoly status, and the assurance of enormous profit margins based on secure metropolitan markets. Private investment, therefore, accounts for much of Africa's modern economic infrastructure. In colonial Africa, a two-pronged investment policy existed: public funds were invested by the colonial governments in roads, transportation, and communication; private investment went into the profitable extractive industries —diamonds, petroleum, iron, copper, manganese, gold, uranium, chrome, bauxite—and into agricultural export products such as rubber, peanuts, coffee, lumber, cacao, sisal. To some extent, and only at a later stage, private capital reinvested some of its profits in service activities such as banking, insurance, and transportation. Very little private investment was made in manufacturing industries. Most of these light industries were established during World War II in order to supply the needs of troops and the large European communities living in Africa.

The coming of political independence to Africa has dramatically changed the position of foreign private investment. In most instances, independence brought with it a sudden stop to the flow of private capital from the former metropolis; in others, it brought a panicky withdrawal of already invested capital funds. Political instability and the lack of investment laws and regulations for private investors created difficult conditions. Much good will, valuable opportunities, and time were irretrievably lost.

Only the international giants in the field of extractive mining continued and cautiously enlarged their investment operations. French, American, and British capital began the construction of an aluminum-bauxite complex in Guinea. The Volta Dam project in Ghana was financed by American and British interests. British and American firms invested in Nigerian petroleum. French and American investments went into Gabonese manganese and petroleum production. The French-German-Italian company Miferma financed new iron-ore mines in Mauritania. A new, large iron-ore field has been put into production in Liberia by American and Swedish interests. In Senegal and Togo, phosphates are being extracted by French and American capital.

Excepting these large-scale investments in mining operations, private investment has shown great reluctance to enter independent Africa. The reasons given are manifold—political instability, limited purchasing power of local markets, pressure to Africanize the local staff, foreign currency restrictions, and lack of convertibility—but whatever they are, the fact remains that private foreign investment is playing a diminishing role in the African effort to modernize. Even the efforts of Western governments to reinsure private investment against possible financial loss have been ineffective in reversing this trend.

D. *ECONOMIC IDEOLOGIES*

African socio-economic underdevelopment has a haunting quality. African governments and the new African elite constantly search for economic and social doctrines that might lead them out of the present misery and despair. They reveal a deep-seated intellectual curiosity to study the causes and effects of the abysmal poverty and weakness of African economic and social structures, and to draw practical conclusions from the analysis. It is only too human and logical that all kinds of more or less utopian ideas find credit alongside established political ideologies and doctrines. Governments, heads of state, political parties both in and out of power, student organizations arrive at different times at different propositions. Governments experiment with various and often conflicting ideologies. Some heads of state identify explicitly with one doctrine; others do so more guardedly and implicitly follow yet another school of thought, or try to harmonize different doctrines in their economic planning. But there is no doubt that socialist thought and experience in its two main branches—Communism and Western evolutionary socialism—has gained a majority of adherents.

It is possible to discern, schematically, three main streams of official African economic thought and action:

1. A minority of African states opt for a school of economic thought that can be classified as "liberal capitalism." States like

Kenya, Nigeria, the Ivory Coast, Gabon, and Liberia have adopted a free-enterprise system, more or less, in which the government encourages and mainly relies on private investment, local and foreign, to expand the economy, regulating and intervening only indirectly through grants, loans, and tax privileges to private economic enterprises. These countries' development plans prove that their main emphasis rests on the encouragement of a local entrepreneurial class, which is given liberal incentives and considerable freedom to dispose of its profits as it sees fit. At the same time, the foreign investor is given the privilege of free convertibility and repatriation of his capital gains into other foreign money markets.

All countries belonging to this category are endowed with important mineral or agricultural resources. On the African scale, they are rich countries. Their mineral and agricultural exports cover and often even exceed the imports of industrial products, thus permitting them to finance important development projects out of their own budgets.

In a strict statistical sense, most of these countries have made important economic gains in recent years. Their per capita incomes are among the fastest-growing in Africa. But the distribution of wealth is scandalously lopsided. A very thin layer of the government elite and the new entrepreneurial class lives in ostentatious luxury—among them the first millionaires in U.S. dollars and pounds sterling—and on the other side of the social structure remain the enormous majority of a tragically poor and destitute population whose standards of living, education, and health have been scarcely affected by the new economic prosperity.

2. The majority group of states are situated from the center to the left of the African political spectrum and can be defined as "experimental socialists": Senegal, Cameroon, Congo (Kinshasa), Uganda, Dahomey, and Zambia. In their opinion, capitalism came to Africa in the form of colonialism, and is therefore responsible for the misery and backwardness encountered today. Capitalism to them means the exploitation of man by man and is a materialistic ideology akin to Communism, since both assume the supremacy of matter over man and are alien to African traditional and religious

backgrounds. Because there is as yet no African bourgeoisie, they believe the introduction of a capitalist system would demand the mass intrusion of private foreign interests and their subsequent hold over the national economy, creating neocolonialism, a new system of indirect colonial exploitation by economic means.

Communism, on the other hand, is rejected as a doctrinaire, atheistic, nineteenth-century Western ideology without roots in the African past and without a response to Africa's needs for the future. Its atheism especially seems unacceptable to the profoundly religious African mentality.

The adherents to this heterogenous left-center group call themselves "African Socialists," and their ideological variations are almost infinite. In the field of economics they are inspired by the examples of Yugoslavia, Israel, and some Scandinavian countries. They try on the one hand to attract foreign investment capital in key industrial ventures; on the other, the state initiates and takes upon itself more and more direct economic responsibilities. In African terms, this means that the governmental administration, through its departments and banks, carries the increasing financial, technical, and professional burden of varied economic ventures in a host of industrial and agricultural endeavors. As part or sole owner of enterprises, it is suddenly confronted with the necessity of running specific economic operations. In an Africa lacking technology, manpower, know-how, experience, and training, this approach was and still is highly problematical, often inefficient, and full of complexities. One result has been to introduce more and more European or non-national technicians to run the government-owned economic enterprises until local staffs can be trained to replace them. This, in turn, creates new problems and tensions. But African socialists regard these complex difficulties as passing symptoms, infant diseases that will disappear with continued economic growth.

3. The third group of states, at the left end of the political spectrum, is composed of Guinea, Mali (until the military takeover of November, 1968), Tanzania, Congo (Brazzaville), and the Sudan, a minority of states that have officially chosen a Com-

munist (Marxist-Leninist) pattern for their economic and social development. For reasons of simplicity they can be defined as African Communists.

We encounter among these states very specific attitudes. African Communism is neither atheistic nor class conscious. No large-scale land expropriation has taken place, nor is the governing political party a highly structured, elite organization patterned on the Soviet or Chinese model. African Communists do not accept the Soviet Union's or China's "big-brother" attitudes. They do not recognize the superior ideological standing of either Moscow or Peking. Frequently, they do not go along with Russian or Chinese positions in international affairs—criticizing them, on the contrary, especially on African political and developmental issues. Any Soviet or Chinese intrusion into local politics through the clandestine support of radical opposition to the regimes has been harshly repulsed and condemned. (In 1963, the President of Guinea, Sékou Touré, expelled the Soviet Ambassador for illegally assisting a teacher's strike; in 1966, Burundi expelled the Chinese Communist diplomatic and aid mission for assisting local opposition groups tied up with the Congo upheavals.)

African Communism's greatest success resides in arousing and organizing the political conscience of an otherwise amorphous population. Through all available means of propaganda and mass media—radio, newspapers, obligatory mass meetings on the town and village levels—African Communism has succeeded in becoming a popular form of government within its national boundaries. From the first, the African Communists addressed themselves to the impoverished public, explaining tirelessly the reasons for their misery, appealing for support, demanding sacrifices, accusing the Western nations of all possible misdeeds and intentions, promoting political consciousness on the village level to an unprecedented degree. The African masses in these countries have been imbued with the idea that any change, any betterment of their living conditions, depends primarily upon their effort and their own willingness for sacrifice. This is, without doubt, the greatest achievement of African Communism to date.

In the field of social and economic development, its results are much less impressive—and often chaotic, if compared to the two other types of government. In two key Communist countries, Mali and Guinea, the economic crises have reached alarming proportions. In 1967, Mali requested of France that it be readmitted into the African franc zone, and Guinea, one of the naturally best-endowed countries in West Africa, experienced between 1965 and 1967 one of the worst possible economic crises—brought on by a breakdown in agricultural production and the wasteful construction of prestige industrial plants that far outstripped investment capacity and the local markets' very restricted purchasing power. Only with the help of massive foreign assistance was the situation remedied. It is interesting to note that the United States, together with the Soviet Union and China, played a major part in this rescue operation. Nevertheless, during the first eight years of independence, more than 400,000 Guineans, mostly of the younger generation, migrated to neighboring countries in search of employment and livelihood.

African Communism has badly failed to prove the validity or superiority of "Marxist-Leninist" thought and experience as applied to African economic development. Agricultural progress has been generally relegated to a secondary position. Ambitious schemes of industrialization under state ownership and management have proven costly and ineffective. The national currencies are almost worthless and inconvertible; money transactions with the outside world revert to one or another kind of primitive barter agreement. The money economy is inflationary to a high degree, and even simple consumer goods are gradually disappearing from the market. A black market is common. The main incentive for work and production is gradually declining.

Lately, African Communist governments have shown greater economic flexibility. Giant foreign interests have received monopolistic privileges in the extractive industries. The American Kaiser-Alcoa group is constructing a multimillion-dollar bauxite-aluminum complex in Guinea. Congo (Brazzaville) has attracted French capital to its tropical lumber industry. European and British interests are prospecting for oil in Tanzania. But the present is grim and the future still uncertain.

E. *THE SEMANTICS OF DEVELOPMENT*

Two African public-opinion polls are of interest in this context. The weekly *Jeune Afrique* (8/1/67), in a poll of 11,491 Africans, discovered that 82 per cent favored socialism and 18 per cent favored capitalism as the best road to economic and social development. And the French-African weekly *Tam-Tam* (November, 1966), in a poll conducted among African students in France, elicited the following response: 37.7 per cent for the "Marxist-Leninist form of socialism"; 29.3 per cent for "African socialism"; 19.7 per cent for a liberal and welfare socialism of the Scandinavian type; 6.8 per cent for a liberal capitalist economy; and 6.5 per cent undetermined.

Nor should we forget that out of 60 political parties in Africa with known and explicit platforms, 43 have opted for a socialist economy, only 13 for a liberal-capitalistic economy, with 4 situated somewhere in between.

Why has socialism in its various forms attracted the great majority of the African elite? In the first place, socialist thought since Marx has vigorously condemned colonialism and imperialism. In the second place, after World War II, socialist movements of all types helped and assisted many African independence movements. Thirdly, the egalitarian concepts of socialist ideology have been able to arouse relatively large masses to the cause of building a modern economy and establishing an impartial and just African society. The example of other socialist states holds great fascination for African intellectuals, and the astounding economic progress of the Soviet Union, Yugoslavia, Rumania, and China, for example, exert a deep influence. Lastly, the lack of investment capital for development and the absence of a local bourgeoisie oblige the African political administrations to posite the state as the major agent for national planning and economic development.

African socialism in all its forms naturally differs greatly from its European or Asian counterparts. But it has succeeded in creating, among the elite and urban population, a mystique of social and economic development strongly underlining the humanistic aspect of socialist thought.

African socialism has a symbiotic quality, a propensity to draw many progressive, traditional, religious, and socialist experiences into a mainstream of political thought and action. Islamic and Christian tenets of faith are freely interwoven with Marxist ideas. Titoist forms of industrial and agricultural organization coexist with Soviet or Chinese patterns or are grafted onto Israeli socio-economic models. French socialist trends and even British labor-movement ideas are given an experimental African test.

But what are the practical results? African socialists can point out that much has been achieved: tribal feudalism has been cur-tailed; legislation against the abusive authority of the tribal elders has been initiated. The rights of women have been advanced against strong opposition from orthodox interests; educational and public-health gains have been registered; government-run market-ing organizations have proven successful; regional political and economic cooperation among states has been instituted and has proven productive; diversification of agriculture has been promoted; producer and consumer cooperatives have been created. Above all, African socialism has succeeded at least in part in interesting the rural population in its own political and social development.

But the dark background of Africa's unsolved problems per-sists. Widespread misery continues to be the lot of the great majority. Urban underemployment is still a major social problem. Government elites have often deteriorated into inefficient, corrupt, nepotic bureaucracies cut off from the nation's economic realities and from the rural masses. Administrations and political parties once capable of interesting and arousing the masses proved unable to channel popular energies into productive action. Disappoint-ment, cynicism, shattered hopes, and increased political tensions are the result.

African socialists did not try to stem the population explosion nor did they succeed in changing the antiquated European educational system or creating new educational structures better suited to African realities. Their limited economic successes were offset by the continued deterioration of world commodity prices, and they were unable to mobilize new resources for compact large-scale investment, either local or foreign. National economic planning was overambitious at first, and much valuable time and capital were wasted in unrealistic "prestige" industrialisation. Here Africa's foreign partners, the Communist ones even more than others, share the responsibility for failure—due to their misconception of the African consumer's low purchasing power and to the rivalry and conflicts between the recipient states.

One illustration will suffice. The Soviet Union constructed a cigarette and match factory in Mali without taking into account two factors: most of the raw materials had to be imported and paid for in hard currencies, and a few hundred miles to the west, in Dakar, Senegal, a rival industry capable of supplying all the surrounding countries with cigarettes and matches had already existed for more than thirty years. Then, for reasons of their own, the Chinese constructed another similar factory in Conakry, the capital of Guinea, some 400 miles southwest of Bamako. And so, three neighboring countries now have three competitive industries all working at low capacity; one alone could have profitably supplied the needs of the whole region. Similar examples abound in many other manufacturing industries initiated and run by foreign interests on a monopoly basis. Their products are generally of low quality, their retail prices twice as high as in Europe and out of reach of the potential African customer—they owe their existence to high tariff barriers and to the purchasing power of the European and Asian merchant colonies.

Other industrial projects see the light of day because foreign economic or power interests were ready, for their own reasons, to invest in the construction of specific industries without regard to national needs and realities. One example may suffice. A few years ago, a modern thermoelectric power station was inaugurated in a West African capital at a cost of $12 million. This station is capable of tripling the country's electrical power output at once.

Neither impending industrialization nor new public consumer needs can account for the remarkable appearance of the power plant. The reality is much simpler. The French-owned monopoly on electricity and water supply in West Africa is affiliated with the builders of heavy electric-power generators in France. In the mid-1960's this industry was in danger of falling idle, due to a lack of orders in Europe and abroad. Financial arrangements that were most advantageous were made with official support, allowing the African state thirty years to repay the investment at an approximate interest rate of only 3 per cent. But ventures of this kind weight very heavily indeed upon the nation's meager financial resources, and their economic usefulness is more than doubtful.

It must be understood that Western economic aid and assistance schemes are all too often inspired by considerations that have little relevance to African needs. Instead of solving economic problems, they create new, more complex forms of dependency, indebtedness, and economic stagnation.

F. CONCLUSIONS AND PROPOSALS

Two tentative conclusions can be drawn. The first concerns the Africans' attitude, and the second, the wealthy industrialized nations' policy on African underdevelopment.

Ten years of African political independence have proven the prime importance of preparing and making the rural populations eager for an all-out effort to improve their lot. This can be initiated by an ideology creating a mystique of human action in the service of economic construction. This ideology must have as its goal and its fulfillment the achievement of social progress for its people. Economic development must be preceded by social consciousness —an almost revolutionary change in popular mentality—which can be brought about only by a new belief in common action based upon a general understanding of the nation's problems. Socialism has provided, for the time being, the main vehicle for a pragmatic African ideology; it has proven capable of arousing popular support and of responding to Africa's need for an intellectual discipline and collective action.

The African peasant has been passive because no one has been able to arouse his interest, to conquer his imagination and win his loyalty. No one ever requested his opinion. Prefabricated solutions to his problems were imposed by his government or by foreign ones. He never fully understood them and they never demanded his active participation. Imposed solutions will always encounter collective animosity, but collective understanding and conscious involvement of the village population will have an electrifying effect upon each individual and upon his community.

The problems of socio-economic progress must be dealt with at the village level. Each villager has to understand the significance of a given project in terms of his own individual interest, as well as in terms of the progress of his community. This work of education and mobilization has to be done by Africans, by men and women the African trusts and understands; no foreign expert can be acceptable. The ideological effort has to be an African affair.

The African administrators responsible for this action should be young, militant, well-educated, and entirely convinced of their central role as missionaries for a progressive economic and social evolution in the service of their own people. African governments will have to engender the mobilization of their own rural and urban populations. They will have to learn to listen to criticism, to observe, and to understand before they take action. Ostentation and class and prestige privileges will have to be foregone until the people's faith in their government has been won. A government leading its people toward political, social, and economic consciousness must of necessity be austere in its public manifestations, open to criticism and suggestions, imbued with the understanding that its historic task is first and foremost to lead the country toward social progress and economic development.

The Industrialized Northern Hemisphere has commitments in (*a*) financing development, (*b*) establishing preferences in aid and technical-assistance programs, and (*c*) elaborating a regional strategy of cooperation.

A. *The Financial Commitment.* In most Western national budgets, expenditures for foreign aid and assistance gravitate between o.4 and o.9 per cent of the respective GNP. It is the international obligation of these nations—and in the long run it is in their enlightened political and economic self-interest—to provide the largest assistance margin possible. Once an assistance quota has been established, credits should be provided on a long-term (at least five year) basis. The fact that most governments are obliged to request new credits for their aid programs at the beginning of each fiscal year creates much uncertainty and misunderstanding. It decreases the planning capacity, efficiency, and continuity of many projects and often defeats its own purpose. Economic and technical cooperation demand long-term commitments in order to assure success and productivity.

B. *Preferences.* Africa's needs are enormous. But in the past ten years, technical cooperation has been offered indiscriminately to too many fields of African activity. Since the recipient nations lacked sufficient investment capital and technical manpower, the impact of the aid was often marginal, inadequate, and finally wasteful. Clearly defined preferences should be established in cooperation with the African nations for each field of economic endeavor. To permit the successful completion of aid projects considered of prime importance, secondary projects will have to be temporarily shelved.

African agricultural development can best be promoted on a regional basis. Agricultural experimental stations, seed farms, and specialized laboratories should be serving climatological and agricultural regions and should not be limited to national borders.

African manufacturing industries will become profitable only if their products can be marketed freely on an intra-African competitive basis, serving the people of more than one state. The limited purchasing power of African populations is a definite barrier to the establishment of national industries.

C. *Strategies of Cooperation.* Ten years of effort have illustrated the need for a strategy of cooperation. Preferences, responsibilities, and targets should be clearly defined. Donor nations too often impose their own economic solutions and social attitudes upon an alien African environment.

1. Public Health. Public health has become the forgotten step-child of African governments. Government budgets have declined, and standards of public and social health are deteriorating rapidly. Public health and education are the two expenditures that weigh most heavily on African budgets; being unproductive economically and politically they pay only remote dividends and are therefore neglected as pressures for immediate spending grow and government incomes decline. In West Africa, tens of thousands of lepers, who were once supported by the colonial governments in specially organized villages, are now crowding into the cities as beggars, showing their open, infected wounds and living from alms. Sewerage systems are neglected, and elementary vaccinations are often not administered. Africa has, conservatively estimated, one physician for every 60,000 people and one public hospital bed for every 450,000. The planning and staffing of an appropriate regional network of public-health centers and mobile health stations is of primary—and humane—importance. This should be accompanied by a large-scale program to train African medical personnel: physicians, midwives, and nurses, working in cooperation with foreign experts. This public-health effort, with its many professional and social aspects, can be realized only with the closest cooperation of African medical authorities. The industrialized nations' commitment to this effort has to be on a long-term basis and has to cover the financial expenditures for an integrated, continental effort that should gradually encompass all aspects of public health and hygiene.

2. Primary and Secondary Education. The illiteracy rate in Africa vacillates between 90 per cent of the population, in the center of the continent, to 40 per cent in the more developed coastal regions. Illiteracy is one of the main obstacles to African social and economic evolution, and it must be overcome in the shortest possible time.

African education budgets are incapable of satisfying the populations' most essential needs, and the African struggle against illiteracy has dangerously slowed down because of lack of finances. Teachers are poorly paid, schools are badly maintained. As African educational systems are modeled on European patterns, it is relatively easy for Western donors to cooperate with African authorities. Here, as in the field of public health, a long-range commitment is necessary.

Eradication of illiteracy in rural areas has been studied, and researched and detailed planning can be undertaken immediately. There is little doubt that the basic needs require first and foremost a quantitative solution of accrued financial investments in school facilities, teachers' salaries, and a network of teacher-training seminars. The primary school system can easily be staffed by Africans themselves, once the finances have been taken care of. In secondary education, large numbers of European teachers will be needed for years to come, but their number will decline proportionately as African students leave the universities for the teaching profession.

The eradication of illiteracy requires a large-scale but gradual approach, relying upon the cooperation of local authorities and religious and private groups. Many details must be taken into account: the African school curriculum should be adapted to African needs and conditions, and should forgo many of its nineteenth-century European characteristics. The antiquated French primary-school system especially should be converted into a semi-technical educational network.

The industrialized nations should undertake commitments in educational development on a long-range basis for at least fifteen years. "White elephant" gifts to African governments of ultra-modern, expensive institutions—whether hospitals or schools—whose staffing and maintenance exceed the budgetary capacity of African governments must be avoided.

3. Communications. The colonial governments left an important economic heritage to independent Africa: an infrastructure of communications—railways, ocean and river ports, highways, airports, bridges, river-navigation systems—but by now the infrastructure is antiquated. African governments cannot afford the huge investments necessary to modernize these public works on the necessary continental scale, yet a modern network of communications is a prerequisite for African economic progress. It is essen-

tial for the modernization of its agriculture and mandatory for the movement of consumer goods and export crops. For the landlocked countries like Chad, Upper Volta, Central African Republic, Niger, Ruanda, Burundi, Uganda, Malawi, and Botswana, whose export commodities must be transported across two or more frontiers and over more than a thousand miles by river and dirt road to the nearest seaport, the situation is particularly desperate.

Tribal diversity, separateness, and animosity have proliferated in a continent devoid of internal communication. African unity, desired by all Africans, will be furthered and established by the solid and physical achievement of opening the continent to the movement of merchandise and men. The example of the nineteenth-century United States is especially illuminating here, as its railroads preceded and prepared the political and economic unification of the continent.

The rich Western nations could further Africa's socio-economic and political evolution greatly by cooperating on an international scale in this task. Their financial resources and technical expertise could be put to most efficient use. Even their weakness for prestige projects could be satisfied.

The proposal to internationalize and concentrate a segment of the rich nations' assistance to Africa into public health, primary and secondary education, and the construction of a continental communication and transport network has the following advantages:

1. It will arrest the gradual disengagement of Western financial aid and technical assistance. Long-term commitments in fields of basic social and economic importance will have to be made and carried out.

2. Western finance and technical expertise will be productively invested so as to benefit all segments of the population. They will not clash with local interests and political ambitions. They will not intrude upon socio-economic experiments that should be conceived and executed predominantly by Africans and that have

proven in the past to be the source of much friction, misunderstanding, and waste between donor and recipient countries.

3. Public opinion in industrialized nations, which has been highly critical and disenchanted with the meager results of the foreign-aid programs, will accept more readily the financial burdens of a concentrated, long-term, and well-documented program.

4. All segments of the African population will come into contact with this historical experiment in international cooperation. Psychologically, this would prepare the African people for the modernization and industrialization of their continent and destroy once and for all the myth that international cooperation is a disguised form of renewed political and economic exploitation and "neo-colonialism." Like medical prescriptions for the ill, foreign aid should be prescribed and administered in exact proportions. Too little is ineffective and finally wasteful. Too much can be dangerous to the body politic. It is the problem of the donor and the recipient to find together the exact proportions needed to redress the problems of the African continent and assist it toward a self-sustaining economy supplying the needs and desires of 250 million people.

December 19, 19—